WARRIORS AT WAR

WARRIORS AT WAR

by

ANTHONY ARMSTRONG

('A. A.')

SECOND EDITION

METHUEN & CO. LTD. LONDON
36 Essex Street, Strand, W.C.2

First published . . April 17th 1941
Second Edition . . 1942

PRINTED IN GREAT BRITAIN

PREFACE

THERE may be readers of this volume who feel that war is too serious a matter for any of its aspects to be treated frivolously. To these the author can only offer his apologies and point out two facts: (*a*) every war, to the British, always does involve a lighter side; and (*b*) the totalitarian states, so notoriously deficient in a sense of humour, are going to lose this one. Possibly these two facts are related. And anyway there's not much about the war in this book after all.

The majority of these articles have appeared in *Punch*, the Proprietors of which journal have kindly given permission to reprint them.

A. A.

CONTENTS

WE ARE READY

W AR has broken out with all its severity, but our battalion is ready for anything in the hostilities line. The reason we are so ready is that only this summer we have been on manœuvres. And pretty strenuous manœuvring we've had too, being buzzed about thither and yon at every whim of Somebody Very Senior. Still we came through without being decimated, or indeed having suffered a single casualty—except Private Sling, who has got 168 hours' detention for firing a blank cartridge at an umpire's horse. The Colonel was inclined to treat it as a mere ebullition of playful spirits, till he elicited the fact that the blank had a lead pencil in front of it. The basic trouble of course was that Sling is one of our crack shots.

Our Lieutenant Holster, it later appeared, had about as interesting a time during manœuvres as any of us. For he and his platoon of merry men were detached as a sort of guard to a special water-supply unit, which in order to give a verisimilitude of real war, had to wander around testing and re-porting on various sources of water. Theoretically most important, but actually, in civilized peace-time England, with Company's water nearly every-where, rather a sinecure. Indeed, Holster says, the unit seemed to spend most of their time testing, though *not* reporting on, various sources of beer.

Holster's job as guard was also rather a sinecure because, although the general idea was that in this restless modern warfare tanks are liable to bob up anywhere in your midst at any time, actually every soldier knows that in manœuvres there is only one tank attack per manœuvre, and when that is due to take place all the military attachés of foreign powers are invariably there to see it. So whatever bloodcurdling warnings an umpire may give about fleets of tanks being reported two points on your starboard bow, you should always look round first to see if the neighbouring hilltops are crowded or not with Liberian generals, French majors, or casual Japanese tourists. If they aren't, then you can tell the umpire to run away and mine himself —under your breath of course.

The tank attack in these last manœuvres of ours did not come to much, largely through an over-zealous military policeman at a cross-roads in the rear who, finding it debouching from a flank, held it up with an enormous hand for half an hour while he let an ammunition column pass. The Portuguese, the Argentines, and the Greeks probably went away saying our police were wonderful; and Holster in his back area knew that he could take things pretty easy for the rest of the time. No one therefore was more surprised than he—and of course the commander of the water- and/or beer-supply unit—when late one evening while supper was cooking, a posse of mechanized cavalry under a sergeant emerged out of a near-by wood and told them they were captured.

When Holster had been at length convinced that
though miles behind the lines the cavalry posse
actually was a hostile one, a long argument ensued.
Holster threw his commissioned rank about a bit
and point-blank refused to be captured: the N.C.O.
tapped his revolver and respectfully insisted under
pain of instant massacre; till finally the sergeant
slowly realized how very, very far he was from
home. He then explained quite frankly that he
had been completely lost since eleven o'clock that
morning and, incredible as it seemed, Holster's
lot were the first troops he'd met. Choking down
the suspicion that they'd captured the *White Horse*
fairly early in the day and had only just evacuated
it, Holster suggested tentatively that the sergeant
allow his posse to be captured instead by Holster's
platoon, and then they could be provided with
accommodation for the night in a barn he pointed
out nearby. The sergeant drew himself up and
said it was *his* capture and that he personally
would die to the last man rather than sell the
honour of a crack cavalry regiment. Or words to
that effect.

The approach of night, however, and the smell
of hot supper from a corner where Private Barrel,
platoon cook, was doing his stuff, induced a more
reasonable frame of mind, and a compromise was
arrived at. Neither, it was agreed, would capture
the other; further, the sergeant would be prepared
to forget he had ever seen Holster, and would
retire with his men to a lonely bivouac in a barn
he had just observed near by. If, in return, some

the latter. Even Colonel Howitzer, when his language became at all decipherable, was heard to admit he'd never seen a parade like it outside of Kipling. A shivering 'A' Company had to unparade hastily and return to barracks later; and now, if you want to live dangerously and know your Rudyard, you've only to mention *The Taking of Lung-tung-pen* anywhere in Bayonet's hearing and see what happens.

On our final checking up, when safely back in barracks at Havershot, we reached the conclusion that perhaps our Lieutenant Swordfrog had after all had perhaps the best time of any one, better even than Holster's. For he, too, wasn't with the battalion at all, being attached, in an information-gleaning capacity, to one of those queer new technical units that our friends the R.E. seem to bud off from the parent body about three or four times a year. Swordfrog says he doesn't know yet quite what it was supposed to be; all he knows is that it was something to do with field survey, which kept it in general away from the battle area. Since, in addition, being an experimental affair, it had no official transport of its own for its various instruments and gadgets, local vehicles had had to be specially hired for the occasion, with the result that it looked like nothing on earth. I mean to say, a procession headed by a Captain on a horse, followed by a small body of armed men, thence passing variously through some grocers' carts, two milk-floats, one highly unpopular wagon evidently used not so long before to carry rotting

6

wurzels or worse, two hay wains, a laundry van, and ending up with a dust cart and a stout quartermaster sergeant, hardly kindles a martial flame in the onlooker's breast.

The R.E. officer, one Captain Nutbolt, had done his best by fixing bayonets to the wheel hubs of the milk-floats and calling them Boadicea chariots, but his handicap was too much. The only thing lacking seemed to be an elephant and a tank. Not a military tank, a performing-seal tank.

At night-time, so Swordfrog swears, Captain Nutbolt formed his vehicles into a defensive circle round his camp—all except the unpopular wagon, of course, which was parked outside and as far to leeward as possible. The milk-floats weren't included, either; they had to be on duty for their early morning delivery and lived some way away in enemy territory. A hazardous journey, one would think, but so simple is modern warfare that they regularly pierced the hostile outpost lines with nothing more lethal than a signed pass from Captain Nutbolt, who, having finished his day's work by forming a laager for his men, normally strolled down to the local with Swordfrog to get another for themselves.

Life passed uneventfully; indeed, only on one occasion, says Swordfrog, was the unit ever even noticed by any one from either side, but Nutbolt had the situation well in hand. It was when an irate Major stormed into their camp circle one night, where the troops were sitting round a good fire—there was a nice bit of forest near by—and started upbraiding Captain Nutbolt for gross dereliction of duty. Nutbolt, assuming that the fire was giving away his position to hostile aircraft, was about to put it out, when he suddenly realized that wasn't the trouble. The fellow was simply a Reparations Officer or something, specially charged to see that no damage occurred to private property, and his line was that there were very strict rules about unauthorized wood fires, owing to Thomas Atkins' complete inability to treat wood whether stacked in a pile outside a house or even in the shape of a wood fence surrounding a garden, as anything but a 'few nice bits o' stick' to be had for the winning.

Swordfrog reports that his opinion of the R.E.'s ability to look after themselves went up considerably when Nutbolt, after hearing the Major out and practically pinning him down to an open accusation of theft, took him to a wagon and showed him therein two large boughs, explaining politely that he knew the rules so well and was so conscious of his duty to his neighbours that he always carried his own firewood with him, legally drawn beforehand from his barrack store.

The Major crumpled, apologized, accepted a whisky, said that he wished all officers were as far-sighted as R.E. officers, and disappeared into the night again—luckily just before the return of one Sapper Lightfinger into the circle with what looked like a gate-post on his shoulder.

And Swordfrog tells us his opinion of the R.E. went up even farther, when Nutbolt explained to him that he invariably went on manœuvres with two large boughs, which were not allowed to be used for firewood on pain of death. They were, of course, strictly reserved for showing to Reparations Officers.

CAPTAIN ABEYANCE AND THE PRESS

WHEN the trumpets of war summoned Captain Abeyance from the Army Reserve to the colours, the change was not immediately apparent, for his surroundings were merely altered from a civilian office in the Strand to the War Office in—hush!—W———l. It pretty soon dawned on him, however, that he was not nearly so well off. Elderly male clerks were hardly the same thing as luscious young blonde typists, while the office furnishing seemed to be pre-last-war-but-three. What annoyed him in particular was an enormous double-doored steel press, holding important files and books and maps. Not only was it quite repellent in itself, but the recent enlarging of his office by removal of a wooden partition had now isolated the press in the middle of the new room, where it looked as unpleasantly conspicuous as the coffin at an Egyptian feast. Moreover, since his office was in the basement it tended to block the already small supply of light. Abeyance wanted it against the back wall and, feeling pretty strong one day after lunch, thought he'd just shove it across. After two minutes he realized he'd misjudged either his strength or his lunch, and took his coat off. . . . After five minutes he gave up, sent for his head clerk, and told him to collect up a few of the merry lads from the other room and shift the thing to the wall.

The head clerk nearly threw a fit. With great respect he pointed out, Abeyance couldn't do *that*. . . . Oh, yes, he went on hurriedly as Abeyance was beginning 'Why the hell . . . ?' he could have it *shifted* all right, anywhere he *liked*, but *not* by clerks, draughtsmen, and so on; it wasn't their duty, in a manner of speaking. Clerks, draughtsmen, and so on's unions didn't permit furniture-removal, which no doubt came under 'Maintenance of Office', and was the Office-Keeper's responsibility. Besides, even if it were allowed, they were used only to grappling with rulers and pencils, not presses. Hadn't the strength, if Abeyance took his meaning. Nor yet the health. Why, old Abbot had a Knee and Burton's Heart was . . . well, not to put too fine a point on it, if the clerks, draughtsmen, and so on started to move that press, Abeyance had better reserve hospital accommodation in advance. Take old Purvis's Stomach, for example, which the doctor had . . .

Abeyance cut short the grisly details, and having ascertained that clerks, draughtsmen, and so on were permitted to handle files and plans and more-over could do so without either dying in agony or falling apart all over the office, told the head clerk to have the press emptied of its heavy contents and then he'd damn' well move it himself.

An hour later the office was thick with dust and ankle-deep in files. Abeyance was struggling once more with the press. After five minutes he again gave up. After five more minutes a thought struck him. He flushed guiltily, looked round to see that no one was watching, and then examined the bottom of the press. With great relief he ascertained that it wasn't screwed to the floor. It was merely that it was HEAVY. So he sent for the Office-Keeper.

Sorry, pointed out that gentleman, nothing to do with him. Maintenance of office, yes. Furniture-moving, no. Furniture came under Office of Works. Good morning.

It was at this point that Abeyance nearly gave up. In most internal War Office manœuvres the Office of Works sooner or later pops up, like the blank wall at the end of promising turnings in a maze. For you can't ring it up, you can't write to it, you can't go and see it, or even ask it over a drink to do something or other for you—not even the things it is its duty to do for you. It is just not allowed. The Office of Works, indeed, is something like the summit of the Matterhorn, remote, high up, and approachable only by skilled climbers knowing and following the recognized route. And the recognized route is through an almost equally mysterious entity called 'Z Branch'.

Abeyance spent two or three days establishing humble contact first with 'Z' Branch and finally with the Matterhorn, and at last was able to inform it he wanted some heavy furniture moved in his office. The Matterhorn replied that it wasn't of course in the furniture-moving line itself, being an Office, but it would get a contractor on the job.

'But,' pointed out Abeyance to 'Z' Branch, 'two or three strong men could . . .'

'Two or three strong men,' cut in Z Branch severely, 'are what furniture-moving contractors are presumed to have, if nothing else.'

Well, well, thought Abeyance, at last he was in sight of the end, however achieved; but he hadn't reckoned with W.D. regulations. No job naturally can be given to a contractor without his first tendering for it, lest he soak the Government after doing the job, instead of before. And further, no job can be put out to tender to one contractor alone: it must be tendered for by several, thus inaugurating a healthy spirit of commercial rivalry.

So when Abeyance, after hailing with delight the arrival in his office one morning of a group of hard-faced men in bowler hats, suddenly realized that they were not furniture-removers, but just contractors offering for the job, he again nearly threw in his hand—particularly when they all produced note-books and pencils and gathered round him with the anticipatory grin of dogs round a butcher's shop. . . .

It is here that the saga of the press assumes the heroic proportions of an epic. Afraid of hurting their feelings, afraid also possibly of being lynched should he reveal the truth, Abeyance shut the door, put his finger to his lips, and in a hoarse, secretive whisper told them that water had been discovered under the War Office, and that they were there to tender for the digging of a well to supply the building in case of air attack and resultant possible failure of the normal supply.

'Where is it, sir?' breathed all the hard-faced men in confidential unison.

'Under there,' replied Abeyance, pointing to the site occupied by the press—and before he could be questioned further, stole out for a quick one. . . .

And that was how Abeyance persevered and got the press moved at last. . . .

It was a pity in a way he couldn't have been more explicit, because they moved it against the wrong wall, where it still is—in, if possible, an even more inconvenient position than before.

But Abeyance doesn't dare bring the matter up again. Besides, all the authorities are too busy tiptoeing about and saying, 'Have you heard? . . . Special water-supply for the W.O. . . . Wells in the basement. . . . They say it's going to cost a hundred thousand! . . .'

GUARDING BRITAIN'S STORES

Letters from the Officer in Charge of a newly opened R.A.S.C. store at Deptfordhithe, to his H.Q.

I

Sir—Now that the Deptfordhithe Store is in working order, I find it to be infested with mice. There *is* a cat about the place, but may formal authority be given, please, for this cat to be brought on the strength. I understand I am entitled to one official mousing cat per 30,000 foot-super of store, and according to the regulations can draw a ration allowance of 6*d*. per day for said animal.

II

Sir—Ref. my Cats/1 of 8th inst., *re* Cats and Cat Maintenance Allowance, may an answer be given, please. We are not now quite so overrun with mice as we were, owing to the fact that several cats are now living here, but these are all unofficial cats. In view of the fact that we are at war, I should be glad to have immediate authority to bring one of them formally on the strength. Also is the decision as to which cat is officially employed to be left to me, or to be given by you? If the latter, I append, for your guidance, a nominal roll of cats now habitually quartering themselves on W.D. property and so liable to military service.

Colour	Number	Name
Ginger	1	'Ginger'.
Tabby	3	'Hitler', 'Goering', 'Goebbels'.
Half-tabby	1½	(see below) 'Cocktail', 'Dago'.
Half-persian	½	(see above) 'Dago'.
Black	4	'Nigger', 'Smut', 'Soot', 'Dirt'.
Kittens, assorted	3	'Kit-kit-kit', or anything.

There are also two casuals, known to us by sight, but they actually live at the adjoining civilian warehouse, and are in no sense likely to make good military cats.

(*Reply to above*)

Authority is hereby granted for ration allowance @ 6*d.*, to be drawn daily for one cat for the store under your charge. This office is not concerned with which cat benefits; and I am to point out that levity is always considered out of place in official correspondence and particularly in war-time.

III

Sir—Ref. your Cats/820/XQ/281 of 15th Sept., your accusation of levity is regretted. The writer throughout twenty years' military service—the

last nineteen with the Reserve—has always under-
stood that everything in the Army—even an
application for Cat-Maintenance Allowance—had
to be treated seriously, and has endeavoured to
do so.

Further to my previous letter, I hereby notify
the formal appointment of 'Hitler' as military
store cat. We had decided on, first, 'Ginger', and,
secondly, 'Cocktail', but as their official rations
were always taken from them by 'Hitler'—for their
own benefit and protection, of course—it seemed
fairer to the War Office to let him have it legally.
Or would this be considered unwarrantable
appeasement?

IV

(*One month later*)

Sir—On perusing the regulations I find that this
store is entitled to possess one dog for purpose of
scaring off possible intruders, spies, etc., at unauthorized times. Ration allowance for this
animal is laid down at 2/6 per dog. Formal permission is therefore requested to take on the
strength one Watchdog of suitable ferocity to
protect W.D. Stores under my charge.

(*Reply to above*)

It would appear that you are entitled to draw
ration allowance at 2/6d. per dog for maintenance
of one W.D.W.D. at your store.

V

Sir—I am not quite certain whether the letters W.D.W.D. stand for War Department Watch Dog or Watch Dog, War Department. To avoid confusion in this matter, though at risk of causing further confusion with the Admiralty, I shall refer in future to 'Towser' as Dogs, Watch, W.D. . . . 1, which to the best of my recollection is the correct Army terminology.

VI

Sir—I regret to enclose the following casualty list, the ferocity of the lately acquired Dog, Watch, W.D. . . . 1, not being tempered with that discrimination one would both have expected and preferred.

Flesh wounds on Leg

Officers	1	
N.C.O.s and Men . .	3	
Postmen	2 (one twice)	

Flesh wounds on Elsewhere

Quartermaster-Sergeants . . 1

Fatal Cases (Excusable under the circumstances)

Cats . . 'Hitler', 'Goering', 'Goebbels'.

I also enclose, in view of above, the following extract from my Daily Orders:

18

Dog 'Towser' resigns appointment as Dog, Watch.

Cat 'Dago' is hereby promoted military cat w.e.f. Oct. 2nd, *vice* Cat 'Hitler', deceased.

Absent without leave: Cats 'Ginger', 'Cocktail', 'Smut', 'Soot', and 'Nigger'.

To Hospital: Cat 'Dirt'.

Under protective custody: Kittens 'Shem', 'Ham', and 'Japheth'.

A replacement Dog, Watch, is being sought.

(*Reply to above*)

I am to direct your attention to the concluding paragraph of my Cats/820/XQ/281 of 15th Sept. *re* levity in official correspondence.

VII

Sir—I have the honour to report that a fresh Dog, Watch, W.D. has been secured and is undergoing a course of probationary training. It has been provisionally named No. 4831 to avoid any further accusation of levity.

VIII

(*One month later*)

Sir—In reply to your Cats/820/XQ/281/5/Dogs/2 of yesterday, I note that the inspecting officer of the previous week comments unfavourably upon the presence in this store of a small black mongrel puppy and requests its removal. This, however, is D.W.W.D.4831, the official watch dog. He is, incidentally, a cross between a Kerry blue and a rather well-born fox-terrier, and so not strictly mongrel.

(Reply to above)

The animal in question can in no sense of the word be termed a watch dog, being too small, too friendly and too fat. Please explain.

IX

Sir—The explanation required by your Cats/820/XQ/281/5/Dogs/3 is that in view of previous experience it was decided to obtain an animal of suitable age for training to the standards of discrimination and ferocity required by a Dog, Watch, W.D. To conform, however, to your comments, D.W.W.D.4831 will in future be referred to by this store as Puppies, Watch, W.D. . . . 1. The question of size and girth will naturally be rectified by the course of time, while the accusation of extreme friendliness is hardly a fair one, as the inspecting officer visited us in uniform and daylight, via the main entrance, not at night in mufti, via a window, and with a German accent.

(Reply to above)

In view of your remarks *re* the D.W.W.D. procured by you, your action must be approved,

20

but under the circumstances the ration allowance of 2/6*d*. per week is reduced to 6*d*. until such time as the puppy can be re-mustered as a Watch Dog. You will kindly arrange to refund for the appropriate period the 2/– per day overdrawn, after which this correspondence will cease, please.

X

Sir—Your last letter will be dealt with by my successor, as I have to-day been ordered overseas on active service.

DRIVER GIRTH DEFEATS A GENERAL

WE have always felt that, even in peace-time, our battalion got more than its fair share of visiting Generals who appeared to be fire-worshippers. By that, I mean Generals who obviously suffered from ingrowing pyrolatry and, when inspecting you, did nothing but pry minutely into your fire-fight arrangements and equipment and then make you put out imaginary fires all over barracks to see what happened. And now, of course, that war has made the putting out of fires even more important, this type of General has simply taken the bit between its teeth.

Well, no names, no pack-drill, but no doubt you remember the General I told you about in another volume who suddenly invented a fire actually *in* our fire-station and *all over* our new fire-engine, simply in order to see us use an elderly and long-superseded manual engine as understudy. He visited us again the other day; but this time, what with the influx of new recruits, he rather met his match. You see he came up against our Driver Girth, and our Driver Girth, who was only called up at the outbreak, hadn't been with us long enough to know much about Generals. Moreover, Girth, fresh from the agricultural depths of West Loamshire, was fat, stolid, and so unbelievably slow in the uptake that they say he had to be put through his squad drill with sticks of dynamite instead of words of command.

It was as a matter of fact Major-General Sir Spurde Feele-Boote's own fault—there, I've told you his name, but no matter!—for he went round to the back of barracks and got into our transport lines. (No one, of course, knew he was meditating an informal visit, or we'd have had a cordon of fleet-footed scouts all round the place from day-break on, each one guaranteed to reach the Adjutant's office and sound the tocsin within fifteen seconds.) Accompanied by his A.D.C., he wandered about, more or less unnoticed, except for an occasional casual salute, and that rather in the nature of a friendly greeting than a tribute to superior rank, for our drivers, who still possess horses in these mechanical days, are as a result an independent bunch. Not that General Sir Spurde Feele-Boote could object. As he so often says, he prefers 'to see the men as they really are'; so, by gosh, if he arrives unheralded in our transport lines, he's getting what he wants.

Then he entered one of the stables. It was empty except for some two dozen horses and Private Girth in his shirt-sleeves, smoking a cigarette. For a time the pair looked at one another, till Girth's brain slowly took in the fact that the newcomer was (*a*) an officer and (*b*) judging by the red and gold about him, a fairly rare one. The mental effort of this, however, told so heavily on him that he was unable to do anything more about it, till the General suddenly barked, 'Well?'

23

Private Girth jumped, started to salute, remembered vaguely some admonition about not saluting without a tunic or cap on, and abruptly turned and went away.

The General called him back and asked him where he was going.

'To get mah coat an' caap,' replied Girth, with a touch of reproof, and the unexpected simplicity of the explanation so surprised the General that Girth was able to find the necessary garments and return, remarking affably as he struggled with buttons: 'You see, zur, I'll be having to salute ye, woan't I?'

The General, still trying to find words, did not answer, and this rather alarmed Girth, never strong on points of military etiquette. He began to wonder whether a salute mightn't be a social error after all. 'Or will I?' he added anxiously.

'You will!' the General managed to get out.

Girth saluted, still with his cigarette going.

'*And* don't salute with a cigarette in your mouth, man!' snapped the General suddenly in such good voice that Girth jumped several inches, lost his cap, threw the cigarette away, found his cap again, and put it on, all in three seconds.

'What would you do if there were a fire in these stables?' suddenly asked the General, choosing his favourite topic of conversation with casually encountered soldiery.

This sort of thing, of course, was right above Girth's head. He merely stared vacantly at the less-inspiring end of a near-by horse, and the General repeated.

Again nothing got home.

'Wouldn't you even *tell* some one there was a fire?' pursued the General, a little more kindly. 'Then the fire-engine could come and put it out.' He was by now plumbing Girth's intellect and realizing its shallow draught.

Girth, however, merely tried the end of another horse and said 'Ar', hastily adding 'zur', as his earlier impression that the fellow might be an officer (which had been driven out of his head by the subsequent give and take of new ideas) suddenly recurred to him.

'Well, there is a fire in this stable,' announced the General clearly, but between his teeth. He repeated it twice, but all Girth did was to revolve agitatedly on his axis and finally salute the end of yet a third horse.

At this point the General left. He felt he just Wanted to Forget. Later he arrived on the barrack square, where he was spotted by the Adjutant, who explained at great length all the fire-fighting arrangements and finally had a practice 'Fire Alarm' for him at the Clothing Store. Whereat what was ostensibly the fire piquet, but actually a squad of our best runners, hastily collected by the R.S.M. while the Adjutant was playing for time, rushed out and did their stuff.

The next move would have been to give the delighted General a glass of sherry in the Mess, but we were frustrated by the entirely unexpected arrival, hot and eager and in full force, of the local civilian fire brigade!

Not even our Adjutant, who's pretty good at impromptu explanations, could get the General to believe this was one of the most efficient touches in our usual fire practice; nor would the local brigade admit they had made a mistake. The situation, already difficult, was not improved by the discovery that it was the delayed-action receptivity of Driver Girth's mental processes that was to blame. Some while after the General's departure, the significance of his last remark suddenly penetrated. With the simple faith of a son of the soil, he went off and informed his sergeant that there was a fire in the stable: yes, he knew it, because an officer had said so some while before, and had told him to tell some one. The sergeant had barely time to take this in, when the practice fire-alarm went off at the Clothing Store, and realizing that this complication would mean even further serious delay, he had promptly rung up the local brigade.

Rescue came from an unexpected quarter. A bale of straw in the stable, in which Girth's hastily discarded cigarette had for some while been smouldering, chose just the right moment to burst into violent flame. . . . The right moment for *us*, that is, but not for a young and inexperienced fire to embark upon its career; for what with our piquet and the local boys it never got a chance. And the Adjutant, who, as I said, is pretty good at impromptu explanations, at last managed somehow to get us the credit for the whole business.

Driver Girth now has an intense admiration for all Generals. 'He toald me right enough there wor a fire,' he goes about saying, 'and I'm beggared if I could see 'un. But *he* knawed!'

LIEUTENANT SWORDFROG SAVES
THE SITUATION

WHILE our battalion here in Ypres Barracks, Havershot, is waiting to be summoned to battle, it frequently has officers from other units attached to it for short periods. Sometimes we become quite attached to them: sometimes we don't—and then we feel that the sooner they become detached again the better. As Major Saddleflap, second-in-command, says, 'we cannot expect to be *uniformly* lucky,' or as our Lieutenant Swordfrog prefers to put it, 'we occasionally get landed with a real stinker'. Such a one (and *such* a one too!) was Captain de Bridoon Crupper, who arrived in our midst last month.

To begin with, he belonged to an as yet un-converted cavalry regiment, and while we of the P.B.I. are broad-minded enough to feel that being in the cavalry shouldn't be openly held against a fellow if he's a decent chap otherwise (which Crupper certainly wasn't), we in return expect him not to treat a line regiment as one of the lower forms of life found under a heap of stable manure —and not even cavalry stable manure at that— (which Crupper certainly did).

For there was no doubt he was a pest. We saw that the very day he arrived and started looking round the ante-room with the air of one who has

often wondered how the poor live, and even now
can hardly believe his eyes. As Major Saddleflap
said, 'not an ideal companion,' or as Swordfrog put
it, 'just a regular b——' But no matter!

Within three days hostilities were in full swing.
When, for instance, Captain Bayonet asked him,
fairly politely too, just what he was attached to
us for, he replied: 'Ostensibly, dear boy, to study
cavalry co-operation with the—ah—common foot-
slogger,' in such a nasty tone that Lieutenant
Holster had to remark to the portrait of Lord
Kitchener over the mantelpiece that he supposed
it *was* more prudent to do it here in England rather
than out with the Expeditionary Force. Lord
Kitchener didn't express an opinion, but Crupper
replied in a cold assertive voice that certain infantry regiments—the names for the moment
escaped him, he added as if they were poor relations
—had in 1918 been only too glad to find cavalry
fighting with them in the trenches, which rather
silenced Holster. Swordfrog, however, took it up
by remarking to the portrait of Lord Roberts
over the other mantelpiece that the infantry had
probably merely been reassured at learning that a
cavalryman *could* effectively come apart from his
horse. He had had some toy-soldiers once which
did that, but they were invariably too bandy-
legged after the operation to stand up. Lord
Roberts made no comment on this either, but
Crupper retorted that if cavalry looked funny
doing an infantryman's job, the other way round
was just a scream. This insinuation made every

one pretty sore, particularly Swordfrog, who only that morning had surreptitiously borrowed the Adjutant's horse and was fairly sore already. So, too, by the way—Swordfrog's riding being what it is—was the horse; *and* the Adjutant, when he found out.

Well, Crupper got worse and worse. Not only did he argue with a self-assertive superiority which made Captain Bayonet look longingly towards the right-hand side of the fireplace where hung two *yataghans*—trophies of the battalion's prowess in Yataghanistan—but worse still he was invariably right, which made Holster and Swordfrog look even more longingly at the left-hand side of the fireplace where hung two *kukris*—trophies of the battalion's prowess in Kukri-bouk. Indeed it was generally felt that if some one couldn't prove him shatteringly wrong in an argument within the next week it'd be a case for both lots of trophies, including probably the culverin hanging in the dining-room —a trophy of the battalion's prowess at the taking of Rumblebellypore.

Then one evening Crupper came into the Mess, ordered a glass of the new sherry from Private Muzzle the Mess waiter, sent it back after tasting it offensively, and later drank it when Muzzle brought it in again in a different glass, because our Private Muzzle is pretty experienced at his job, and doesn't like the cavalry, anyway, ever since a horse trod on his backside at manœuvres.

'Queer animals you infantry fellahs have round here,' began Crupper loftily. For a moment we wondered whether he was trying to insult our transport lines, till we remembered that Crupper was never rude to a horse.

'Never thought to see a zebra on what you so humorously call your recreation ground,' he went on.

Bayonet pointed out that zebras usually lived in Africa, and Crupper reminded him that they only originated in Africa, but having four legs— in case Bayonet didn't know—might occasionally travel.

Bayonet was glancing yearningly at the *yataghans* when Holster suddenly came out into the open.

'We bet you,' he said firmly, 'a free drink every time we meet in the Mess that you didn't see a live zebra on . . .'

'And I take you,' cut in Crupper quickly, 'all of you. My statement is that this afternoon I was standing at the gate to the recreation ground, looking out diagonally across to the pavilion, and I saw a live zebra.'

There was a moment of real excitement over this. Evidently he'd had a couple and got incautious. Every one felt we'd caught him at last. Lieutenant Surcingle rushed for the book in which bets are recorded, and Bayonet even ordered a round of the new sherry—for all except Crupper. He refused, remarking pointedly he'd unfortunately tried some already.

'Of course,' he went on, 'I'll back up my statement with documentary evidence, dear boys. I happened to have two films left in my camera and snapped the animal. Boots are developing them and I'll bring 'em in to-morrow night.'

There was then a moment of real chill. Every one now felt there might be a catch in it after all. Bayonet tried to cancel his rashly enthusiastic round of sherry—but without luck: Bayonet doesn't push the boat out so often that we could let him get away with that.

Later that night, when Crupper had gone, we discussed the probable catch at length, even to wondering whether some of those limbs of buglers hadn't cut loose with a pail of whitewash on Surcingle's black mare. Strictly speaking it didn't make her a zebra, but would be hard to prove.

It was Sergeant Grenade who inadvertently revealed the catch next morning.

'Funny about that zebra, sir,' he volunteered to Swordfrog, during a break in parade.

Swordfrog flinched, but came up to it bravely. He then learnt that a zebra had escaped the day before from a passing circus on the road near the recreation ground, and had been at large for two hours. This put a new complexion on matters, and Swordfrog felt that some deep thinking by the P.B.I. was called for. . . .

We were none of us very happy gathering in the ante-room that night and noticing the package from Boots' photographic department in Crupper's pigeon-hole. And when he came in and said to Holster as he opened it, he thought he'd have a Martini from him instead of sherry because at least one knew what it was made of; and champagne later from the rest of us, things looked black. . . .

We crowded despondently round the snaps. Four were private ones; two showed the recreation field. But in each case it was bare of any animal of any sort. . . .

We had quite a cheery evening after all. Bayonet concentrated on wondering out loud what Crupper could have had for lunch that had made him see non-existent zebras in empty recreation fields; and Swordfrog was airing a theory that the cavalry should be mounted on zebras for the next war to make them a better target for long-range guns; while Holster kept quite simply going out of the Mess, coming in again, and, in the terms of the bet, 'meeting' Crupper.

It wasn't till next day that we put our finger on Crupper's real mistakes, that of (a) describing so exactly just when he'd taken the photo; (b) not allowing for the fact that Swordfrog had a camera of the same size; and (c) not realizing that Swordfrog knew a man in Boots' photographic department rather well. Well enough, in fact, to ask him to do little substitution as a joke. . . .

As I said earlier, when we are not attached to those who are attached to us we feel that the sooner they are detached the better. But in this case we were quite sorry that Crupper went so soon. After all, free drinks in a Mess like ours are free drinks.

LIEUTENANT HOLSTER GETS HIS

OUR Lieutenant James is normally the Mess Secretary, but during the last fortnight he was away on a street-fighting course or some other pleasantry, and an understudy had to do the job. Of course, the chance was too good for us to miss, as the following extracts from our Mess Complaint Book will show.

Complaint. (*11.7.40.*) Suggested that the Acting Mess Secretary bring formally to the notice of Lieutenant Holster that the undersigned officers consider his behaviour while playing bridge after Mess in the evenings leaves much to be desired. In particular, they would like attention directed to his custom of chewing absently at his 'hand' while waiting his turn, with the result that several of the cards are badly nibbled by the end of the evening. While it is annoying enough for the other players to find that certain cards in their hands have had their corners masticated, it is even more annoying to suspect that they have perhaps been masticated in such a manner as to indicate their identity to the masticator.

> (*sd.*) G. Bayonet, Captain,
> and Five others—ex-
> clusive of Lieutenant
> Holster.

Complaint Ignored.

Complaint. (*13.7.40.*) *In re* our complaint of
11.7.40, it seems that either no representations have
been made to Lieutenant Holster, or that, if made,
they have been ignored; for the ace of spades was
eaten practically down to the spade last night.
It is now further suggested that the officer in
question be provided each evening with 'Soothers,
babies' . . . 1,' by way of curing him of this distressing habit.

> (*sd.*) G. Bayonet, Captain,
> and five others—still
> exclusive of Lieut.
> Holster.

Answer. (*14.7.40.*) The Mess Secretary sug-
gests that you all think you're very funny, don't
you?

> (*sd.*) J. Holster,
> Mess Secretary.

Complaint. (*14.7.40.*) Suggested that in the
previous complaint the words 'Soothers, babies'
. . . 1,' be amended to 'Soothers, officers', with
ribbon . . . 1.'

> (*sd.*) R. Swordfrog, Lieut.

Complaint. (*14.7.40.*) I concur with the above.
This solution would also prevent Lieutenant
Holster's usual inept post-mortems after every
game, and his usual inane chatter during it. It
would further prevent his saying, 'What? Is it
my deal?' prior to every fourth game.

> (*sd.*) G. Bayonet, Capt.

Answer. (*15.7.40.*) Quite unnecessary, thank you. J. H.

Complaint. (*16.7.40.*) Suggested that, if 'Soothers, officers'' are considered unnecessary, the trouble may be more deep-seated—or is it deeper-seated?—and that every avenue should be explored to find something on which Lieut. Holster can exercise his teeth during bridge—particularly those two ugly ones that stick out like a rabbit's. Might not the real trouble be diagnosed as hunger-pangs? Even though we start playing bridge quite soon after Mess, one must remember the quality and quantity of the food which the Acting Mess Secretary sees fit to supply.

(*sd.*) R. Swordfrog, Lieut.

Answer. (*16.7.40.*) The quality of the food supplied is invariably excellent. J. H. Mess Secretary.

Complaint. (*17.7.40.*) The fish at breakfast this morning was distinctly 'off'. Please see this does not occur again.

(*sd.*) A. Howitzer, Lt.-Col.

Answer. (*17.7.40.*) Deeply regretted. This is being looked into at once. J. Holster, Mess Secretary.

Complaint. (*17.7.40.*) Sycophant! R. S.

Complaint. (*18.7.40.*) After rising from to-day's lunch I certainly agree with the diagnosis of Lieut.

Holster's trouble as hunger-pangs. I suggest that he be provided in the evenings with one plate of biscuits per rubber—at his own expense. He may even—though this seems a lot to expect—prefer them to the club and diamond court cards which appeared to attract him so strongly last night.

(*sd.*) G. Bayonet, Capt.

Answer. (*18.7.40.*) The Mess Secretary points out that the Complaint Book is for reasonable complaints and/or practical suggestions—not for frivolous comments. J. Holster, Mess Secretary.

Complaint. (*20.7.40.*) I do not agree that the previous writers' complaints can be called entirely frivolous. As a married officer and therefore a non-dining member, I have not actually played bridge with Lieutenant Holster. But I lent him a pencil the week before last and when I got it back I found the end had apparently been savaged by a starving hyena. Capt. Bayonet's suggestion, therefore, seems to me very practical, though perhaps biscuits hardly meet the case. They would not last long enough. I personally would suggest a good tough steak; and in this connexion the Mess Secretary could not do better than hunt up the one I was given at lunch two days ago. It should be somewhere about, as after ten minutes' fruitless struggle I threw it out of the dining-room window—the one at the far end. It bounced off a fir tree into the big clump of bracken near by. A search should soon reveal it; for I cannot imagine that any dog would be misguided enough to tackle it—not even the extraordinary mongrel one is always falling over outside the Mess, which I am told belongs to the Acting Mess Secretary. (Has it really got mange, by the way, or is that just where it rubs its shoulder daily getting in and out of the Mess dustbin?) And even if a dog has tried that steak, I don't think he will have damaged it much. I now remember my pencil had a rubber on the end of it when lent to Lieut. Holster, but not when returned. In that case the steak should be just the thing for him; it very definitely *bounced* off the tree. Perhaps it was *really* a rubber one, solely for shop-window display and included in the Mess order by mistake?

(*sd.*) A. Saddleflap, Major.

Answer. (*21.7.40.*) The Mess Secretary thanks Major Saddleflap for his comments, which in view of the difference in rank he feels he cannot answer as fully as he would like. And as you know, sir, it isn't mange, he caught his shoulder on a tree while chasing a rabbit.

Complaint. (*22.7.40.*) The corners of both the ace of hearts and the two of clubs went last night. R. S.

Answer. (*22.7.40.*) Three new packs of cards have been issued to the card-room to-day. J. H.

Complaint. (*23.7.40.*) What has happened to the Mess cards? Playing bridge last night I could not recognize one of them. In particular the absence of the two familiar canine tooth-marks on the King of Spades led me to an error of play which lost me 15/4 on the evening.

(*sd*.) G. Bayonet, Capt.

Answer. (*23.7.40*.) Action held over. The Mess Secretary returns from his course to-morrow. Thank heaven.

(*sd*.) J. Holster.

(*23.7.40*.) We concur.

(*sd*.) Major Saddleflap,
and eleven officers.

FULL CIRCLE

SOME while ago our Captain Bayonet had a brainwave. Strangely enough, he was on a Board of Officers at the time, hardly, one would think, a good forcing-house for even brain-ripples. Not only, however, did Bayonet have a really fine brain-billow, but it actually got taken up by Those in Authority. The fact that it ultimately developed in the peculiar way it did is not really Bayonet's fault: still, he can't help feeling a little responsible somehow.

It began in the early days of the war when the War Office got an idea that various military store depots were becoming overcrowded with large quantities of obsolete stores, which ought to be got rid of to make room for something more in the correct battle-waging fashion. Judging from the circulars sent round they seemed so het-up over this question of obsolescence that our Lieutenant Swordfrog suggested they must have been coming across inventories with items like 'Arquebuses', and 'Shot, chain,' and possibly even 'Axes, battle' still listed thereon. Anyway, the net result was that one morning Bayonet found himself part of a Quorum of Officers inspecting a big Store Depot at Havershot, during the course of which they discovered in a far top corner, called Bay 82, an enormous pile of metal canisters, refills for gas-masks.

'Why aren't these down below with the others?' asked the President, the King of the Quorum, as it were.

'Ah, sir,' explained the aged Head Storekeeper, stroking one of them lovingly, 'these are Mark VIII and obsollit. . . .'

'Ob—what?'

'Obsollit. The downstairs ones are Mark IX. What they use now,' he added disparagingly, 'being as how there's a war on. 'As a slightly different top or some such!'

The Storekeeper was an ex-Quartermaster-Sergeant, and like all Q.M.S.'s, his conception of a store was something between a private art-collection and a bank strong-room. That is to say, getting him to part with any item was like tapping him for heart's blood, which explains why he had such an affection for the Mark VIII canisters. Being obsolete, they were never issued, and he could count them every week and find them the same as it left him in the pink, whereas any Tom, Dick, or Harry could walk in with an indent and carry off scores of his Mark IX's at a blow, on the flimsy excuse that their lot were under orders for France.

'Well, *they'll* have to go,' said the Quorum Boss. 'That's something, anyway.'

'Seems a waste,' added another. 'There must be about a million of them.'

'No, sir,' corrected the Storekeeper austerely, for this was right up his street. 'Sixteen thousand, seven hundred and forty-two and four defective.'

41

Then it was that Bayonet had his brainwave. 'If there's only a slight difference in the top,' he pointed out, 'why shouldn't we recommend that they be sent to a factory to be altered and re-issued? It'd save the W.O. some money. Not,' he added bitterly, 'that they care!'

'Good idea!' said the Quorum, and so Bayonet's brainwave was incorporated in their report. They left the Storekeeper tearfully regarding his beloved Canisters, Gas-mask, Mark VIII in an agony of impending separation, and looking rather like a mother-cat who knows her kittens are doomed to be drowned.

Well, the brainwave went up through the usual channels, was adopted (and credit taken for it) by Somebody Very Senior, and in due course the firm of Messrs. Tinspot & Co., Ltd. were given a contract for the adaptation and supply. Each week, thereafter, two thousand at a time, obsolete Canisters, Gas-mask, Mark VIII were formally issued by the Storeman to the Tinspot Works, there altered as to the top, and ultimately returned to the Store as up-to-date Canisters, Gas-mask, Mark VIII*.

.   .   .   .   .

Some three months later Bayonet happened to be in the same Store on business. While waiting about, he had a look upstairs at Bay 82, rather in the manner of a proud father, whose son has now gone to school, taking a peep at the old cradle in the box-room. Bay 82 was bare, except for a forlorn label reading 'Canisters, Gas-mask, Mark VIII', on which some bygone humorist, evidently a student of Stores' Lists, had pencilled:

> 'Arrows, Bow . . 20
> Arrows, Agricultural . 1
> Arrows, statue of, see Cupid
> Arrows, in spelling, see above.'

'Ain't 'alf 'ad a time, sir,' puffed the Storekeeper, suddenly bustling up, 'over those Canisters, Mark VIII. Keeps me right on the hop.'

'But you've got rid of them all now, I see.'

'I have, sir,' replied the old man proudly. '*And* two lots more. Second lot's going away to the factory this minute, and I'm just expecting a third batch in.'

'I—I don't quite understand,' faltered Bayonet.

'Well, it's like this 'ere, sir. As soon as I found how quick they were getting through those obsollit Mark VIII's, I naturally indented for more, or I'd get choked off for letting my stores run out. But the Tinspot Works finishes up what they've got in hand before I get 'em in, and then *they* get a choke-off for the delay in delivering the noo Mark VIII*. They then says they can't get the obsollit Mark VIII's from me, 'anding me the baby-like. Luckily I can say I've indented for 'em but that the firm supplying Mark VIII's have let me down. So *they* gets a choke-off for not . . .'

'But,' asked Bayonet in a choked voice, 'who *is* the firm still supplying obsolete Mark VIII's?'

'Same firm, I believe, sir,' replied the storeman

casually, as one to whom it was a mere detail. 'However, I've got the job taped now and we run as smooth as . . .'

Bayonet merely put his hand to his head and staggered out of the place in a coma.

Things certainly were running smoothly as the Storeman had said. For, as he went, he saw a Tinspot lorry piled high with Mark VIII canisters for conversion to Mark VIII* passing out of the main gates, while at the delivery side of the Store another Tinspot lorry was just unloading the third lot of new Mark VIII's that the Storeman had ordered.

So you see that Bayonet can't help feeling a little responsible, but he hasn't the vaguest idea what steps to take about it. The thing is just too big for him. So far all he's done is to buy a large number of Tinspot, Ltd. Ordinary Shares. He says he thinks the firm has prospects.

THE PASSING OF THE BATTALION
ACCOUNTS

ONE advantage of the war has been that a lot of strange officers have popped up from the reserve and are temporarily attached to us. What I really mean is, they've brought new stories into the Mess: we were beginning to know all Colonel Howitzer's and Major Saddleflap's by heart.

Last night, for instance, one Lieut.-Colonel Girthweight pulled a beauty out of the bag, while we sat discussing Hitler and port.

Some while ago, it seemed, he'd been commanding a battalion in India for the first time, and at the end of the financial year sent up the regimental accounts to the Command Paymaster for approval. Now in England this generally means a short correspondence on various points raised, and after explanations and adjustment the accounts are ultimately passed—with perhaps a friendly rap on the knuckles about some dubious outlay 'for military requirements'.

In India, however, Colonel Girthweight found it difficult. Having got the accounts off, he received in three days a polite acknowledgment, and nothing more. He naturally assumed that the matter was closed, and in fact was delighted at encountering such unparalleled amity and trustfulness.

He hadn't, of course, then realized that most of

45

the routine machinery of Indian life is in the hands of the Babu, a native clerk with a high-powered English education; nor that it is run by him with a meticulous attention to detail and an intense love of verbal argument.

He was therefore considerably surprised to receive after three more days a letter signed by the Command Paymaster, running to five pages, and commenting vigorously on every aspect of the accounts. There was hardly an item of expenditure that wasn't turned inside out and held up to the light, and the whole document dripped with queries.

For some time the Colonel tried to reconcile the Command Paymaster's well-known love of polo, as a distraction from his office labours, with the fact that he must have spent twenty-three hours out of every twenty-four in the office to have composed that letter in the time. Then his eye was caught by phrases like 'and, oh, sir, if this be so, it would appear that a serious defalcation must be raising an occulted head like a snake in the night', and 'in item 7 there is a lurching *suggestio falsi*'. At which he realized that the Command Paymaster hadn't done much more than formally sign the letter between 'chukkers'.

After two days' solid conference with his Pay Sergeant, during which they tried unsuccessfully to compose an answer, the Pay Sergeant reported sick with a nervous breakdown, while Girthweight went to see the Command Paymaster in person.

'Answer it how you like,' said the Command Paymaster, impatiently tapping his riding boot with a crop at the door. 'My head clerk, Babu Ram Das, drafted it: he won't mind what you say!'

'Can I tell him what I think in person?' asked Girthweight hopefully.

'Lord, no! You must answer it formally!'

'But I haven't the time—my Pay Sergeant's sick—my orderly-room clerks don't understand finance—my . . .'

The Command Paymaster looked at his watch. 'Got to go in a minute, but I tell you what. Borrow a clerk for a day from my office here. They're well up in the subject . . . Whoa, there, Kitty! Whoa! . . . Er—so long! . . . *Sais!* Why's that damn' martingale so tight. . . .'

Left alone Colonel Girthweight waited a moment, then strode into the clerks' room. . . . Next morning from the Command Paymaster's office there reported at Battalion H.Q. for what he called 'a day's loan duty *in re* financial consultation over unaccountable accounts' no less a person than Babu Ram Das himself. He was handed his own letter, and without a smile on his shiny brown bespectacled face sat down to give it 'some earnest perusalling'.

'Oh, sir,' he reported later. 'This letter has made many slip-ups. To take one exemplification, it is not strictly within the Command Paymaster's authority to persecute an inquiry into this item of one rupee eight annas for . . .'

'All right, Babu,' said Girthweight politely. 'You go ahead and draft an answer!'

By that evening a lengthy document awaited

Colonel Girthweight's signature. It was a masterly refutation of every point raised and it blew through a myriad cleverly discovered flaws in the original criticism like a gale through wire-netting. The Colonel signed it, thanked Ram Das, and considered the matter closed.

He little knew. A week later he got another letter from the Command Paymaster—'while accepting, sir, some of the discriminations levelled at the head of my CP/A420/81/1Z of 14 ult., I have honour to postulate hypothesises "A" to "K" as hereinafter undermentioned . . .' and so on. The Pay Sergeant took one look at it and ran another temperature. The Colonel swore at Babu hypocrisy in general and Ram Das's baseness in particular, till he suddenly realized the matter was in his own hands. The next move was up to him. So he 'phoned over and borrowed Babu Ram Das once more.

Babu Ram Das excelled himself on this occasion. He tore the letter figuratively to shreds; he found obscure financial regulations and quoted them at the Command Paymaster. In fact, he wiped the floor with him, and the Colonel was almost afraid to sign the letter, except that he now knew who the real recipient would be.

After this, of course, he wasn't surprised to get a shattering reply from the Command Paymaster, and even though this one was signed 'R. Das, per pro C. P.'—the polo competitions being in full swing —he felt it was quite in order to borrow the Babu's service again for an even more shattering retort.

Being himself busy when it came up to be signed, Ram Das obliged for him as well, and so he did not see it. It must, however, have been a real winner, because the correspondence abruptly ceased.

Or so Colonel Girthweight thought.

Three months later he suddenly came upon a 'Battalion Accounts' file six inches thick, with the latest letter dated only the previous day. He then realized that Ram Das had merely cut out the figureheads in the business and had been trotting back and forth between the two offices, corresponding busily at himself all the time, and, in short, revolving round his own axis with increasing centripetal energy. . . .

'I tried to stop it,' Colonel Girthweight told us in conclusion, 'by ringing up the Command Paymaster and asking if he didn't need Ram Das's undivided services, because I didn't want to see him again. All he said was, no, he could spare him easily, as owing to increased pressure of work these last months he had now a brother of Ram Das employed in his office as an additional clerk. And that evening Ram Das came up and said that in view of the increased pressure of work in my pay office he had advised the Adjutant to take on a full-time civilian clerk, "a verree good man and a Failed B.A.—my nephew, sir." . . .

'At that I gave it up and a week or two later I was retired. But for all I know the file's going on still and providing by now for most of Ram Das's family. . . . More port, any one?'

DANGER AVERTED

TWO new motor-cycles were delivered to our battalion last month, replacing two 'unserviceable' ones. The transaction was a direct result of optimism—optimism displayed by Sergeant Plug, the instructor, in assuming the previous week that Privates Muzzle and Pullthrough were fully competent to take their road test. It was not even as though a bomb had dropped near the barracks to which we could have cheerfully ascribed the damage. Though the result looked much the same, it was just Privates Muzzle and Pullthrough.

Still, it didn't matter, for the Army's mind works in a peculiar manner, even in war—or perhaps particularly in war. Once you have been formally issued with a motor-cycle you can smash it up completely, without being censured, as long as you indent for a new one in the proper fashion and have a reasonably plausible excuse—such as, of course, Privates Muzzle and Pullthrough. What you cannot do is lay a finger on the crate it comes in; for it belongs to Ordnance and might as well be constructed of solid gold. So when the Adjutant noticed Private Butt, a battalion cook, hovering round the newly arrived crates with an innocent look on his face and a small chopper behind his back, he at once gave orders that they were to be securely locked up in an empty hut. There they stayed for three spring weeks, while he made arrangements for their return—no doubt with a band and a guard of honour—hoping that a bomb wouldn't drop on the hut, because, where crates are concerned, the Ordnance rarely believe in bombs.

The great day came and a small fatigue party, under Sergeant Grenade, entered the hut, gave a 'Together heave!' at the first crate—and came out again in an enormous hurry, the cause being a swarm of bees which, entering by the window, had just taken up new quarters in the crate. Sergeant Grenade, by the way, was observed to be occupying the post of danger in the rear; not, however, in the approved military tradition, but simply because he hadn't the same turn of speed as his men.

In a short while Lieutenant Swordfrog, the Orderly Officer—in response to an SOS—drove up in his car. With him he brought the Barrack Officer. They ventured cautiously to the window and looked in. The bees were swarming in a bunch on the wall. 'Ah, bees!' said Swordfrog cleverly, turning to the Barrack Officer. 'What are you going to do about 'em?'

There followed a long and interesting argument. Swordfrog maintained that bees on a War Department wall were a barrack fixture, and the Barrack Officer ought to remove them. The latter held that bees on a War Department wall were merely a dirty wall and the battalion ought to clean them off. At this Sergeant Grenade moved a cautious pace to the rear: he guessed who'd be detailed for the cleaning off. The Adjutant then came up —our Adjutant is never out of anything for long— and announced, as usual, that the whole thing was a 'nice point'. Since bees, he pointed out, could actually be kept officially in some stations, they should therefore come under Ordnance. If, however, they had already *made* honey, it was definitely a supply question, and the R.A.S.C. would have to deal with it. Should, on the other hand, the bees be traced to anybody, it was a case of livestock trespassing on Government property, and they could be impounded until replevied. Sergeant Grenade here took another step backward: he guessed who'd be detailed for the impounding.

Captain Bayonet, who had now come across from his office near by, volunteered that a 'swarm in May was worth a load of hay', and Swordfrog quickly added that in that case they might be traded off for the benefit of the Adjutant's charger which, owing to excess of oats, was perhaps a little more mettlesome than . . . The Adjutant, who had had conspicuous trouble with 'Bucephalus' on the last formal parade, here fixed Swordfrog with a steely eye and abruptly changed the subject. He said had they all forgotten that the C.O. was coming round inspecting war equipment with General Blind-Bloodberry. He added that all bees, honey, and/or forage, had better be got out of the way, because it looked like being a stinker of an inspection, anyway, it being the General's month for finding fault. He then stalked off,

52

saying, as a parting shot, that he'd blame Sword-frog if the General were displeased at anything.

It was at that point that Private Barrel entered the story. One of the fatigue party, he had been passing the time by larking about at the back of the hut with Private Sling. During this he missed his balance and fell against the side of the hut. Now Private Barrel is no gossamer; when he falls against the side of a hut it is rather as though that hut had been charged by a Mk. II Light Tank, especially when it is hit by that part of Private Barrel which looks most like part of a Mk. II Light Tank. The walls shook and quivered, a splintering sound was heard at the point of impact, a pane of glass fell out of a window on the other side, and the close-knit swarm of bees apparently burst outwards.

Within three seconds all that remained of the fatigue party was Private Barrel, who'd naturally been delayed, and even he was doing a steady twenty-two up the road in the wake of his commander. Bayonet was miraculously back in his office, peering through the window with the hastily assumed air of one who'd been working there all morning and had just that moment casually got up to see if it looked like rain. Swordfrog, apparently in a cloud of bees, was in his car, hastily winding up all the windows. He managed this with such speed that only three bees got in too. He then sat very still, hoping these three wouldn't notice him. The other bees began to range about vindictively.

5

Suddenly in response to gesticulations from Bayonet, he saw that farther up the road the C.O., looking miserable, and General Blind-Bloodberry, looking eagerly for something to find grievous fault about, were approaching in ignorance of their fate. Moreover, he remembered what the Adjutant had said about holding him to blame.

So hurriedly slamming the car into gear he drove to them and started to explain by gestures. But to his horror the bees, which were all round his car, *came with him*. For a moment his two superiors stood their ground: then they broke and ran in opposite directions. Swordfrog, still thinking of the battalion's fate, and his own, should the General get stung, followed him with the idea of getting him inside the car. Unfortunately the bees continued to follow—so thickly that Swordfrog could hardly see to drive and as near as a toucher ran the General down, till he got his windscreen wiper going. Wherever the General led Swordfrog followed, and wherever he went the bees went too.

At last the General, wildly yelling and flapping his hands, reached his own car near the Orderly Room and went off home like a rocket, Swordfrog here abandoning pursuit.

The battalion was saved from adverse report because the General hadn't begun to inspect. Moreover, he never came near us for three weeks, by which time it was his month for approving things. So Swordfrog had saved the situation— or rather the bees had by following him about.

Just *why* wasn't at first apparent—till the three that were in his car got out through the roof ventilator and the swarm suddenly left for foreign parts. Then Swordfrog realized that one of those in with him must have been the Queen!

ONE HORROR OF WAR

'THIS is the Cartography Department, War Office. Captain Intray here.'

'Oh, who is that, please?'

'This is the Cartogr——'

'Oh, I was asking the exchange for somebody who's something to do with maps.'

'That's quite right. Cartography Department speaking. Who are you, please?'

'Oh, well, my husband asked . . . I mean, I'm speaking for General Sir Cust Gore-Ruddier, of Dera-Doon House, Guildford.'

'Oh, yes, certainly.'

'He's down there, but I'm up in London at the moment. Who did you say you were?'

'This is Captain Intray.'

'Oh, do you know the General? Of course he *retired* several years ago. . . .'

'I'm afraid I haven't the pleasure. But what can we do for him?'

'Oh, he wants a map.'

'What map does he want?'

'Well, it's *rather* difficult to . . . Well, a *war* map.'

'Er—excuse me, but it isn't any map you could get commercially—buy outside, I mean? You see, this Department of the War Office only has authority to . . .'

'Oh, no, not the kind the General means, you can't. But he *knows* they have them at the War Office. . . .'

'Perhaps he could apply by letter? We're terribly busy here, you know; the war keeps us at it.'

'Oh, I know; isn't the war terrible. The General says that in his opinion . . .'

'So if the General would write in officially . . .'

'Oh, but he sent me up *specially*. He thought I could explain so much *better* just what he wanted. . . . Did you speak?'

'No, just clearing my throat! Excuse me!'

'Besides, it's urgent. I mean, it's needed *to-night*. That's really why the General asked me to ring up the War Office, because I was coming up to town, and find out from you if you'd got what he wanted, and then I could come round and fetch it, and as long as I started back in time to avoid the awful black-out, I . . .'

'Quite, quite, quite. With the pressure of work we have here, I wanted to find out how important the matter was. Just what map do . . .'

'It's not wanted for fun or anything, if that's what you mean. It's a work of, well, almost national importance, you could call it.'

'Oh, of course. Just what map is it that's wanted? You understand, naturally, that many of our war maps are secret and can't be issued to civilians—er—to officers not actually entitled to be issued with them.'

'Oh, *naturally*. What I say is, we've got to be

careful. Look at the spies in the last war, how they . . .'

'Hrm! What was the map?'

'Oh, a war map.'

'Yes, but what front, or part of the front? We have hundreds of maps here and we *are* very busy.'

'I *know*.'

'And if you could let me know the scale?'

'The scale?'

'Yes, the size of the map.'

'Oh, a very big map.'

'I mean the relative proportions of . . . Er— did the General write down what he wanted?'

'No. And I'm certain he didn't say anything about *scales*.'

'Oh, well! What part of the front do you want?'

'It doesn't really matter. Just a war map.'

'Doesn't really matt—— Perhaps you could tell me what war?'

'Oh, any war.'

'*What?*'

'It's for a lecture he's giving to-night.'

'Oh, *I* see. Er—have you any idea what war the General proposes to lecture on?'

'Oh, yes. It's his usual lecture. And all the local Boy Scouts. . . . .'

'Yes, but what *war*?'

'The lecture's called "My Waziristan Days", but he illustrates it with a home cinematograph film of troops on manœuvres in 1925, showing how the basic principles of military tactics and strategy . . .'

'Exactly, exactly. Then do I take it he wants a map of Waziristan?'

'No, it doesn't matter, I tell you. He wants just a war map, one of those very large war maps that you used to have. Ours has got holes in it. The General's found by experience that when hung face up to the wall, the back of them makes the ideal screen for his cinema pictures. . . . What did you say?'

OUR CAPTAIN BAYONET

THESE two stories about our Captain Bayonet occurred long before the war, but the fact that there is a war on now is not going to prevent my telling them. After all, as Bayonet himself says, 'Anything *I* do is interesting, war or no war.' He then stands you a sherry before you can accuse him of boasting. And at a sherry a boast Bayonet can even tell us how he personally conducted the Retreat to Dunkirk if he likes.

Well, you may remember my explaining in another book how Bayonet once passed his inter-pretership examination in Slwuggagond, an obscure Indian dialect originally taught him in infancy by his ayah. This is the story of how Bayonet, when last the battalion was stationed in Singapore, did *not* pass his interpretership examination in Malay.

He undertook the business, of course, in the true spirit of the British officer who unselfishly wishes to increase his value to his country—and at the same time is not unmindful of the fact that a monetary grant is awarded to those who pass. Indeed, Bayonet was so busy arranging in advance how to spend his grant, that the day of the examination was only a month away before he suddenly realized that the Malay he possessed might not be adequate to the occasion. It was, in short, largely confined to telling 'boys' to bring him a drink and

not to take an unprintably long time about it, or
to explaining that his car was *not* going too fast,
and that the price of a scraggy dead chicken thirty
yards back up the road could not *possibly* be
twenty dollars, even if it were tame and the apple
of the speaker's eye—and even if the speaker
were the owner. So he at once embarked on an
intensive course with a *munshi*, or native teacher of
languages.

Now a *munshi*, among other things, does a
considerable amount of letter-writing for the less
educated of his immediate circle. This means he
has a fine command of the language on paper, but
is not generally so hot at teaching by word of
mouth. Thus by the time of the examination
Bayonet's prose had a flowery picturesqueness
which, as long as he remembered to keep out
phrases like 'Houri of a Thousand Delights', and
'Thrice Ill-omened son of a pig!' would probably
carry him through the first, or written, part. It
was the second half, the *viva voce*, that was
worrying him.

The *viva voce* exams in Malay are conducted thus.
Two Malay leading citizens of unimpeachable
character are approached by the Army and asked
to be examiners. They sit in a room and the
candidates are loosed in upon them one at a time.
The Malay gentlemen then converse about this
and that, taking care to make the candidate do
his share. Then they allot suitable marks, and
eventually go home to a well-earned meal.

A senior British official is also present to keep a

fatherly eye on the proceedings—ever since the occasion when it was discovered that Mr. Ali bin Awong, one of the leading Malay citizens selected, was a leading citizen by virtue of being the biggest moneylender in the town and, in fact, numbered several clients among the candidates for examination. The rest, as far as Ali bin Awong was concerned, were potential clients, and so the *viva voce* interviews ran on somewhat unorthodox lines. As far as could be ascertained later, every candidate who was a client passed very high up, on the unspoken understanding that the interpretership grant should be used to reduce his indebtedness. So did every other candidate who agreed to become a client at a powerful rate of interest. It was from Ali bin Awong's point of view a series of heaven-sent business interviews, and no one would have known anything about it had not his co-examiner given him away two weeks later, on being tactlessly pressed to knock something off his own particular account.

As a result the exams, as conducted under the British official's aegis, were now merely a series of conversations based on uncontroversial news items in the day's papers; and when Bayonet discovered this he brightened up. He had, he informed us in the Mess a few days before, an idea which would ensure his passing with distinction. In fact, he was willing to bet on it, and we all took him up, the currency used being gin *pahits*.

The great morning came and went, and several of us went down to the Club to meet Bayonet for a pre-lunch cocktail and find out how he had got on.

'Of course the results aren't *actually* out yet,' he announced loftily, 'but I've passed on my head!'

We asked how he could be so certain, but he refused to tell us till just as he was leaving.

'Well, if you must know,' he began, in a superior tone, 'it was like this. First of all I applied for private and personal reasons to be interviewed last.'

'Why?' asked Swordfrog.

'Because there were nineteen other candidates, and I guessed the examiners would have completely exhausted the newspapers and be at their wits' end for a topic of conversation. So I presented them with one . . .' His voice trailed away. We saw his eye had been caught by a pretty girl sitting in a car outside the Club and trying to make the self-starter work.

'Eyes in the boat, please!' said Holster. 'What did you do?'

'Eh? . . . Oh, yes . . . I put my arm in a sling just before I went in. They jumped at it. "What, sir, is wrong with your arm?" they almost yelled. "Sirs, I broke it two days ago," I replied modestly in fluent Malay. "The radius is unharmed, but the ulna has a double fracture near the wrist. I improvised a splint and went to hospital, where it was X-rayed. After it had been set by the doctor, who assured me that no complications were likely to supervene, a plaster-of-Paris . . ."'

'All this in Malay?' asked Swordfrog awed.

'Why not? I had the speech pat, with every technical word I could think of . . . Dammit, I'd been up all night learning the stuff. There wasn't a Malay word about arms, fractures, hospitals, or doctors I didn't know. They hardly got a sentence in edgeways. Of course I *may* only have got ninety-nine out of a hundred, I think I mispronounced one word. . . . May I help?' he broke off gallantly to the lovely in the car.

'Oh, I couldn't trouble you! My father will be out in a moment and he'll give her a swing . . . Oh, it's too *kind* of you. . . .' For Bayonet, ever susceptible, was swinging the engine for her.

He'd just got it going when a voice broke in. It was 'father', and 'father' as Bayonet looked up, was the British official who had just presided at his examination.

'For a double fracture of the ulna, young man, you swing a car remarkably well,' was all father said. . . .

And that's why Bayonet didn't pass. To this day if you ask him the Malay for 'fractured ulna' you have to run like hell.

The other story about Bayonet has to do with a certain Statue. It happened when Bayonet, then a subaltern, was stationed at a small African trading post called Bongawheli, engaged on surveying for a new road. Accompanied only by a few skilled N.C.O.s, he was finding life good; for it was quite uncomplicated by generals or even colonels, or indeed anything more threatening than the two local traders, the local police officer, and the local difficulty of keeping one's drinks cool.

Then one day he was informed that a rather important Colonel was coming to pay them a formal visit of inspection. Free as he had been of colonels for so long, Bayonet felt quite kindly towards them, and by the evening, when he and his friends had had a couple, they were all saying what Good Fellows colonels were and how they'd like to do something to brighten up this chap's visit.

This was before dinner. It was during dinner that the rather surprising suggestion was made of erecting a statue in the centre of Bongawheli to greet the Big Man on arrival. It came, however, from one of the traders, who for years had had a big statue taking up space in a store farther down river. He'd long ago forgotten how it came to be there: he only wanted to get rid of it. By the end of the dinner it had been enthusiastically agreed that this statue should in future adorn Bongawheli, and the further brilliant suggestion was made by Bayonet—long after dinner, in fact *en route* to bed—that the jolly old Colonel should be asked to unveil it.

In due course the statue—a sort of Grecian female—arrived and all Bongawheli turned out to greet it. It looked pretty awful lying on its side on the river bank, as one arm was outstretched and gave the figure rather the impression of having dropped off to sleep in Green Park. It was not so bad, however, when tentatively set upright, but quite what it represented no one knew; for the eyes appeared to be glaring fiercely downwards and the uplifted hand now seemed almost menacing. One of the traders said, Ah, that was symbolism, that was; but when asked just what he meant, he said he didn't know. Bayonet eventually volunteered that the statue was probably Justice— Justice seated and (he went on lyrically) regarding with infinite scorn and restraining uplifted hand the petty jealousies of the humans beneath. The police officer was quite moved and said let it be a statue representing Justice and Fraternity as between black and white in Bongawheli. With which he took a running kick at his grinning black servant for bringing him an empty siphon.

As military representative, Bayonet was put in charge of the actual erection of the statue, while the police officer undertook to arrange the parade of local personnel, and the traders said they'd each lend a gramophone from store for the band.

Looking back on it now, Bayonet admits that they *were* carried away a little by their own enthusiasm. But the monotony of life at Bongawheli was such that when the chance of a break offered itself they rather lost their sense of proportion.

The Colonel, too, evidently realized this, and quite entered into the spirit of the thing. At least, after he'd recovered from the shock of arriving at one of the farthest outposts of Darkest Africa and being promptly asked to unveil a statue next day.

But, as the police officer pointed out, it really would impress the natives, who'd been coming in from the bush for miles around to attend the ceremony.

Next day saw the native police and Bayonet's men drawn up in three sides of a square, with crowds of natives jabbering excitedly away behind, In the centre was the statue on a pedestal, swathed from head to foot in store blankets and looking imposingly amorphous; while on the fourth side was the flagstaff, with the police officer, Bayonet and the Colonel, who had been raised to the status of Big White Chief for the day, grouped beneath. In front of the Colonel was a table covered with a Union Jack and bearing a tumbler of water, a small gavel and an enormous polished press button. To one side waited the two traders with their gramophones ready for a simultaneous start.

The Big White Chief made a short speech. 'Unaccustomed, etc. . . . the honour devolves on me, etc. . . . privileged to unveil, etc. . . .' He was a good linguist and the natives fairly ate it up. He ended with a grand peroration stating that the statue was to stand for ever as a symbol of the attitude of the white races towards their black brothers. He then solemnly pressed the brass button.

Bayonet gave a loud and pointed cheer. The two traders got their gramophones off on the National Anthem to a perfect start, and the blankets over the statue parted and fell slowly to the ground.

Now the natives, who hadn't been able to under-stand at all why the statue which they'd seen openly for the past week should on this day have been covered up, had by now come to the con-clusion that it must be part of a stupendous con-juring trick. Indeed, a travelled gentleman who'd been as far as the coast, got a great following by explaining that it would no doubt have changed into a rabbit—or rather, he added, keeping the thing on the right scale, an elephant. At any rate they all expected something pretty much out of the ordinary would be revealed.

They weren't disappointed. The statue, it seemed, had during its period of retirement ac-quired a new symbolism. There was, in fact, a notable addition, making it, instead of a symbolic statue, a symbolic group. For at its feet there was now the figure of a small black boy, presumably representing the native races. But its face was buried in its hands, as if to avoid the scornful stare of the statue's eyes, and its small behind pointed upwards as if about to receive chastisement from the menacing upstretched hand. To put it briefly, the whole character of the Statue of Justice and the attitude of the white races to their black brothers had changed.

For a moment a breathless silence hung over the assembly, broken only by the weird jazz effect of one trader's gramophone establishing a lead of a half-bar over the other at 'send him victorious'.

Then Bayonet clapped his hands and uttered a furious malediction in the native tongue. The lower half of the statue came abruptly to life, gave a scared glance round, scrambled up and whizzed off into the crowd like a small black bullet.

As Bayonet said afterwards, he'd never known natives could laugh like that. Anyway, it was just as well: knowing nothing about formal unveilings, they'd have been terribly disappointed if after everything it'd been just the same statue as before; probably it would have started up a riot.

'But,' he explained to his friends, after the Colonel had passed on, 'I'd told the little beggar to crouch at the foot of the *pedestal*, not of the statue.'

'*Why* have him at all?' asked the police officer.

'Because you put me in charge of the unveiling, didn't you? Well, he was there to cut the rope when the Colonel pressed the button. Don't you realize the nearest electricity is seventy-five miles away?'

LIEUTENANT SWORDFROG AND THE LEAKY ROOF

FOR some two very wintry months our battalion has been stationed in a new semi-permanent camp at ——— hush! Well, all I can say is it's somewhere on the East coast, where we are exposed to the full force of a peculiarly unpleasant wind which we call a 'North Sea Special'. It is a wind which blows very hard and almost horizontally and, to save time, carries its own rain with it. At such times any roof which is not made of corrugated iron, bolted and plugged at every pore, is apt to leak like a shower bath.

This fact the local contractor, who under R.E. supervision was just finishing off the camp when we arrived, had fully recognized, for a more depressing collection of solid iron-roofed living-boxes couldn't be imagined. The only building uncompleted was the H.Q. offices, and as soon as our Colonel Howitzer realized this he made such a fuss about not having an indecently naked tin roof to his H.Q. that he actually got his way. The plans were changed and the building topped off with a beautiful red-tiled roof in Oriental-Surbiton-Tudor; though the R.E. 'demurred' politely and the contractor kept darkly muttering that something he called 'Nammysis' would take a hand later.

If he meant it would leak he was right, because

when our first North Sea Special arrived two days later, rain just poured through the ceilings of every office in the H.Q. block. In a wet fury Colonel Howitzer rang up the R.E., and, skilfully brushing aside as irrelevant all references to the original corrugated-iron design, he concentrated on the point that the R.E. were mere passengers in the military boat if they couldn't make a simple ordinary roof watertight, and they'd better repair it immediately.

Within an hour Colonel Howitzer, now busily working, found his office invaded by a large number of the contractor's workmen who, in a lumpish dreamy way, settled down to drift about the room, smoking cheap fags and waiting for their foreman to tell them what to do. Colonel Howitzer at once seized the 'phone—hampered slightly by the foreman who was trying to stand on his desk to see where the water had come from—and flared off into it, somewhat unreasonably, that when he said immediately, he didn't mean *now*, when the rain had *stopped*, he meant during the *week-end* or at *night time*, or any other time when he wasn't *there*, and would the R.E. at once call off their tame crazy-gang till some more opportune moment.

In a short while a breathless R.E. corporal arrived and removed the party till next Saturday afternoon, the party being definitely all for this idea, seeing that it meant overtime rates.

During the week-end men swarmed over the bungalow roof like beavers. During the following week came another North Sea Special. During the North Sea Special the rain again came through the roof. There was, however, a definite improvement, in that it only came through into one of the offices this time. Unfortunately the office was Colonel Howitzer's, and secret files and documents swam about his desk like goldfish.

In answer to his SOS, an R.E. subaltern, a sergeant, and a picked gang arrived at the double. Colonel Howitzer interviewed the subaltern at heated length, and went back to the Mess for the day. The shattered subaltern, after creeping about the small space between the office ceiling and the roof, and crawling all over the tiles outside, ended by directing repair operations in person from the roof ridge. Down below the sergeant was hastily making good a hole in the Colonel's ceiling, where the subaltern had inadvertently miscalculated the position of a joist.

Came the next 'North Sea Special'; came a lot more rain; came a lot more water on the Colonel's desk. And when after more repairs it happened yet again, we began to pray for a bomb to drop on the building. Or, of course, Howitzer might explode with apoplexy with approximately the same result. Life in the Mess, of course, was absolutely unbearable for all of us.

It was about this point that Lieutenant Swordfrog came into it. An elderly, wrinkled inhabitant with one cunning eye buttonholed him outside the Mess after breakfast, and in practically unintelligible local dialect announced that he did hear tell as how rain couldn't be stopped from leaking through the ceiling. . . . Here Swordfrog, scenting both kudos for himself and relief from an intolerable situation in the Mess, which was making visions of of the front look like play-hour in a Kindergarten, asked eagerly if he were a roof-mending expert.

The old man admitted that he was in a manner of speaking, in that he thought he could keep the rain out of the Colonel's office, but that his method was a trade secret.

Swordfrog almost fell on his neck, and feeling that the Mess would back him up on the financial side, at last arranged that for twenty-five shillings the 'expert' should get on the job after dark that night, so that his secret process might not become public; and further, that he should be paid five shillings for a weekly inspection of his handiwork and any necessary maintenance. This was the old man's idea, but Swordfrog had jumped at it. In his experience of similar experts, so far from actually undertaking to see that their work was what it promised to be, they generally asked for an advance 'to buy special materials' and then were never seen again.

Next morning the old man reported that everything was now all right; and after an anxious half-hour when a 'North Sea Special' came two days later, Swordfrog realized that it really was so. Colonel Howitzer came in beaming to lunch, and Swordfrog's stock was high. By the evening he was going about, throwing a chest and saying: 'Takes an ordinary fellow to do an ordinary job; these R.E.s are far too specialized.'

North Sea Specials came and went all that month, leaving the Colonel's desk, and the Colonel, unaffected. The old man also came and went, regularly but mysteriously, every week. We felt our five bob was being well spent. At last Swordfrog got so curious as to the nature of the secret formula that he couldn't resist climbing up one Sunday afternoon into the rafters. . . .

When he came to think of it, he realized that the old man had never said he could *repair* the roof, merely that he could keep the water out of the Colonel's office. And he had. For just over the place where it had come through there now stood a large tin hip-bath. Weekly maintenance simply meant the 'expert' regularly came and emptied.

We decided we wouldn't tell the R.E.s after all. They're really too technically-minded to understand. Nor did we tell the Colonel: in fact, we continue to feel it's cheap, when all is said and done, at five bob—especially as we are now making Swordfrog pay it.

THE NEW MESS SECRETARY

Letter from Adjutant, 1st Loamshires, to Second Lieutenant Tunic, Mess Secretary, Officers' Mess.

The C.O. wishes me to point out that whenever he has come into the Mess latterly something or other is wrong. Yesterday there was some trouble about a new Mess waiter and the gravy: to-day he tells me he found all the blotting-paper on the writing-table chewed and nibbled. I fully appreciate that you have not had much service so far: at the same time if you find your ordinary Regimental duties so onerous that you are unable to give adequate attention to your job as Mess Secretary, I shall have to afford you more time. An obvious method of so doing occurs to me on observing the frequency with which, in spite of the fact that the country is at war, your name appears in the Short Leave Book.

(sd.) L. W., Adjutant.

From Mess Secretary to Adjutant.

Sir—I am very sorry about the C.O.'s complaints. The Mess waiter who spilt the gravy twice over him at lunch tells me he did it from nervousness, not knowing anything about waiting. It seems he was detailed for the job by Sergeant Grenade under a misapprehension, because he was a plate-layer by trade.

As regards the nibbled blotting-paper, I cannot understand this. It may have been some more nervousness on the waiter's part, after Colonel Howitzer had spoken to him.

M. Tunic, 2nd Lieutenant.

From Adjutant to Mess Secretary. Two days later.

You are to take every step to stop this infernal nibbling that goes on in the Mess. The Colonel says that to-day it was the Mess envelopes, the Visitors' Book and a copy of 'Imperial Military Geography'. What *is* it?

From Mess Secretary. Three days later.

Sir—Mice.

Answer, on margin.

What *are* you talking about?

From Mess Secretary to Adjutant.

Sir—I am answering your question of last week. It is mice that are nibbling things in the Mess. They had Private Trigger's (Mess waiter) cotton gloves last night, owing, he says, to some mutton fat on them. Traps seem of no avail. What should I do?

Answer, written all across foregoing.

Get a cat, man, get a cat. Ask your Company Commander if you want help. Don't keep on bothering me!

Letter from 2nd Lt. Tunic to his O.C., Capt. Bayonet.

Sir—The Adjutant told me to get a cat for the
Officers' Mess because mice are eating things—
gloves, blotting-paper, geography books, etc. He
said I was to ask you if I wanted help. How
should I set about this, please?

From Capt. Bayonet to 2nd Lt. Tunic.

If you wish to be issued with 'Animals, Protective, for W.D. Property,' you should indent
officially on me, and I will forward it to the proper
quarter.

State definitely whether you want 'Cats, Rat'
or 'Cats, Mouse'. It *might* be rats, if they eat
geography books.

*From Capt. Bayonet to 2nd Lt. Tunic. Two days
later.*

Indent received. Please find herewith *Cats,
Mouse, Tabby . . . 1 (Male)* and issue voucher (to be
receipted) for same.

*From 2nd Lt. Tunic to Capt. Bayonet. Three days
later.*

I am not absolutely certain about the feeding of
this cat. It is a *very* fat cat, and seems to want a
lot of milk. It also likes fish: it had Lieut. Holster's
at breakfast yesterday.

From Capt. Bayonet to Mess Secretary.

'Cats, Mouse,' are official Army Cats, on the
ration strength. Submit the demand for rations

through me on the normal scale of *Milk, Pints, per Cat, Mouse, per day* . . . $\frac{1}{2}$. It should, of course, only eat *mice*; and you should tell Lieut. Holster not to give it fish, however much he loves animals.

From 2nd Lt. Tunic to Capt. Bayonet.

Ration demand for *Cats, Mouse* . . . *1* herewith. *N.B.* Holster did not *give* it fish: it jumped up when he wasn't looking—and I rather gathered at the time he does *not* love animals.

From Capt. Bayonet to 2nd Lt. Tunic.

I forgot to tell you that should the cat not have finished its milk at the end of 24 hours, the unexpended portion of the day's ration must be brought on charge next day. Also that a return of Mice caught on Govt. Property has to be filled daily in triplicate.

From 2nd Lt. Tunic to Capt. Bayonet. Later.

We have only two mice so far and we rather think one was not caught by the cat but trodden on by Private Barrel, cook, when it was eating cheese in the larder, as it has rather a flat look and some cheese crumbs on its whiskers. Besides, the cat still eats things in the kitchen. It tried the mess breakfast bacon the other day, but could not seem to find a rasher it really liked. The Mess Caterer said it didn't matter as none of the officers would notice.

Did *you* notice, by the way—Wednesday morning, the day I had a boiled egg?

From Capt. Bayonet to 2nd Lt. Tunic.

You should report to me in duplicate all cases of tampering with food, whether by mice or Cats, Mouse. And please note that in future I shall require boiled eggs only at breakfast.

From 2nd Lt. Tunic to Capt. Bayonet. Four days later.

Sir—There was evidently some mistake about the '*Cat, Mouse (Male)*' issued a fortnight ago. I beg to report the arrival of *Cats, Mouse . . . 5* (*sex probably various*). Do I apply for extra rations?

From Capt. Bayonet to 2nd Lt. Tunic.

The mistake was purely typographical. *Re* my letter of 10th instant, for '*Cats, Mouse . . . 1 (Male)*' please read '*Cats, Mouse . . . 1 (Female)*.' Error regretted.

Rations for '*Cats, Mouse . . . 5*' are in order, but note that Allowance Regulations lay down that rations for the day of arrival can only be claimed for 'troops disembarking before noon'. Time of disembarkation should therefore be verified.

From 2nd Lt. Tunic to Capt. Bayonet.

The Colonel wants to know what I am doing about mice in the Mess, as the Army List has now been nibbled. Just off to see him—thought I'd let you know.

Very hurried note from Capt. Bayonet to Adjutant.

For Heaven's sake stop young Tunic from seeing

the Old Man. I've been having a game with him about a cat in the Mess and was collecting a grand file to show you, and now the C.O. will see it.

From Adjutant to Capt. Bayonet.

Too late, old man, he's seen it. Now he wants to see *you.*

LIEUTENANT SWORDFROG AND THE CANADIANS

WELL, the Canadians are over here in E——d once more, ready again to do battle. A battalion of them is encamped quite near to ours, and we have lost our Lieutenant Swordfrog. I don't mean we've lost him in the way one frequently loses things when camped near Canadians—those three bicycles at Gavrelle in 1917, for instance—we've merely lent him to them for a fortnight's liaison and bear-leading duty.

He came back yesterday, and for the moment is quite unbearable, just *too* Canadian. He slouches about in the Mess in a studied 'loose-limbed' manner, which only knocks people's glasses over; he speaks like a cross between Gary Cooper and Horace Horse, his idea of the accent; and he is constantly referring familiarly to Mounties, trappers, and the Far Frozen North as if the snow were hardly dry behind his ears.

However, we are working on him. We now have a poem beginning:

> Flat of foot was 'Canuck' Swordfrog,
> Flat of foot and fish of feature,
> Shooting off his mouth before us,
> Codlike in an armchair lounging. . . .

There is a lot more of it and when it gets *really*

personal later on, Swordfrog stalks angrily out of the room. At which we tell him to come off it and have a small fiawatha and soda with us for Gitche Manitou's sake! This only makes him more furious than ever. Like the Mounties, we always get our man.

He brought back one good story, though. It seemed there was one of the Canadian officers who'd been getting pretty much on the others' nerves for weeks. He was a Great Traveller. He was a Broadminded Man of Experience. He was a Citizen of the World. He knew Canada from Esquimalt to St. John's, and called all the United States by their nicknames. He'd always visited six places which any six men with him hadn't. He also talked largely about the three-thousand-mile undefended border between Canada and the U.S.A.; and in contrast—his big theme, and greatest crime of all to his brother officers—he was highly scornful of France, England, Belgium, and the other little European countries with hardly any space for a man to move about in, and yet hedged off from one another by absurd gun-bristling frontiers, passport systems, currencies, and the like. He was, in short, an unpleasant fellow to live with.

Swordfrog arrived in the Canadian Mess just as some of them had found an opportunity to teach Lieutenant Moccasin a lesson. 'He's so full of himself, we guess we'd better empty some of it out,' they explained to Swordfrog, who found himself apparently in on it. For the occasion was a trip that three officers, Mocassin being one of them, had to make by road and in mufti to a seaport somewhere in E——d and W——s, well, to be precise, somewhere in W——, and Swordfrog was going with them as liaison officer, and general dogsbody.

They had passed through Hereford, going West —sorry, through H——d, going W——t—and were approaching the borders of—oh, never mind the Censor!—Wales, when Captain Mapleleaf started the ball by saying to Mocassin:

'Soon be in Wales now. Got your passport ready?'

'Say, do we really need passports?'

'Naturally. You're in plain clothes, not uniform.'

'But for Wales, I mean?'

'Well, of course. We're in Europe now!'

'That's right,' confirmed Swordfrog when appealed to, pulling his out ostentatiously. 'I should have told you, but I thought you knew.'

'Sure! You're a travelled man,' added Lieutenant Birchbark, sailing a little near the wind.

Not that it mattered. Mocassin was already well away on his favourite theme, ending up by wondering why in hell every fiddling little county in England didn't have a customs barrier of its own and be done with it. They let him gurgle out like a bath-waste and then held a council of war on the situation.

'Got to get you through somehow,' said Mapleleaf. 'What do you suggest, Englishman?'

'Well, they're not too strict on this part of the

border.' Swordfrog had been well coached. 'They *may* not examine the car, if we handle them right.'

'I get you. We'll hide him in the back. How far off are we?'

'About a mile.'

'Then we'd better start now,' said the other grimly.

Moccasin protested, but never suspected. It was so exactly the sort of thing he constantly inveighed against. Passports to go into Wales, indeed!

They made him crouch down on the floor in the back—after an urgent debate as to whether it wouldn't be better to lock him up in the boot. They covered him with rugs and piled two suit-cases on him. With a touch of genius Birchbark arranged a petrol tin so that the corner stuck into his ribs. Then after solemnly winking at each other all round, they warned him not to speak a word, and drove on. Mapleleaf took his time over it and selected all the most uneven parts of the road. Suitcases, petrol tins, and Moccasin bumped and jumbled together in the back. Whenever he swore under his breath they angrily hissed him to silence.

Round about the Welsh border—at a likely looking pub—Swordfrog was inspired to say: 'There's the frontier post!' in a clear voice. They all got out.

'Not a move!' growled Mapleleaf to the suitcases, 'or we'll all be in jail.'

It was a nice pub. The beer was good and from

the warm interior they could see the car outside. After twenty minutes Swordfrog began to feel sorry for Moccasin, but Birchbark said grimly: 'You haven't had him in the Mess for two months,' and ordered another round.

As a final touch they got the landlord to come with them to the car and speak loudly in Welsh, while they said things like, 'No, nothing to declare,' and, 'Nice of you not to trouble to look at the car.'

They drove on. After another mile of bumpy road they let Moccasin up for air. He was a sorry sight, red-faced, stiff, gasping, and cold. There was very little fight left in him, but his friends, it seemed, hadn't quite finished.

'That was a damn' near thing,' said Mapleleaf, 'when that guy wanted to examine the car.'

'I had to slip him a pound for drinks to let us past,' put in Birchbark swiftly. 'You might hand it over, Moccasin, will you? It was done on your account.'

Moccasin, wanly petulant about the venality of the minor officials of third-rate countries, handed it over so easily that Mapleleaf decided to cut himself in.

'And two pounds for me while you're at it,' he said. 'I thought you wouldn't want to be without the right money so I changed some for you into Welsh. Got twenty-five and a half harlechs to the pound too.'

Again the grumbling Moccasin paid out. . . .

'A pity,' said Mapleleaf to Swordfrog that night, 'that you couldn't get in on any dough too. Still, there'll be one fine row when he finds out and tries to get it back.'

'When are you going to tell the others?' asked Swordfrog curiously.

'Oh, *we're* not. *He*'ll do it himself, two minutes after he gets back—if he doesn't write to the papers first. Petty European restrictions, three thousand miles of Canada and U.S.A. . . . You know his line. Oh, boy, what a night that'll be! And then I bet he'll never, never mention frontiers or European countries again. Well, suits *us*!'

MONGOOSE, SNOOKER, KING BEAVER

IF ever you come to dinner on a guest night at our Officers' Mess at Ypres Barracks, Havershot, and if ever you happen to look at the labels on the three port decanters as they are pushed round the table afterwards, you'll see that, instead of Light Port, Vintage Port, and so on, they bear the legends 'Mongoose', 'Snooker', and 'King Beaver'. The next thing you'll naturally do is to ask what these mean, and two fellows will just have started to tell you when the President will announce the toast of The King, and in the subsequent general rush for the best dishes of fruit in the middle of the table, the whole matter will drop.

So by special request our Captain Bayonet has for the first time committed to print, before it shall be lost in the mists of time, the original story of how our ports—ports, mark you, no better and no worse than any other battalions' ports—came to bear those damfool names.

.   .   .   .   .

One wet October afternoon in 1922 *(writes Bayonet, who hasn't yet acquired the arresting 'A shot rang out' school of fiction)* three officers, Major Saddleflap, Lieutenant—for even Napoleon was a corporal once—Bayonet, and Lieutenant James were assembled in the Mess ante-room when they

87

were suddenly informed by the Caterer that Messrs. Cherry & Co., Ltd., Wine Merchants, had sent three sample bottles of port to be tested, tried, and approved or otherwise by the Mess Wine Committee. As it happened, there was at the time no official Wine Committee, but Major Saddle-flap, who was then acting as President of the Mess, did not lose his presence of mind. Within two minutes there *was* a Wine Committee of which, strangely enough, Major Saddleflap was President. Even more strangely Lieut. James and Lieut. Bayonet had been invited to sit on it with him.

The Committee promptly took steps and a corkscrew, and began to sample the first bottle. Major Saddleflap tried a glass; Lieut. James tried a glass; Lieut. Bayonet tried a glass. It was proved good. At this point Lieut. Holster suddenly entered from the billiard-room (where he had been playing with Second Lieut. Swordfrog), saw the port before it could be hidden, and so had unfortunately to be co-opted on to the Committee. He took a glass. It worked. He took another. That worked too, and he began to tell a story. The story was the story of a mongoose. No one has yet been able to understand that story, largely because Lieut. Holster has never had quite sufficient time to complete it. It needs really more time than one can spare all at once in the Army, owing to parades, leave, transfer to other stations, and tours of foreign service. It'll probably be the longest story ever told—if ever told.

Briefly the story—as far as known to date—is

that a man was travelling in a railway train with a bag. In this bag he asserted he had a mongoose. The train came to a wayside station, where another traveller got in and after a while said, 'What have you got in your bag?' (At this point Lieut. Holster took some port.) The first traveller replied, 'A mongoose.' The second remarked 'Oh!' and just then they came to another wayside station. (At this point Lieut. Holster took some port.) A third man got in and soon afterwards the second traveller said to the first, 'Do you know that *I* have a snake in *my* bag?' and the first man said, 'Oh!' and they came to another wayside station. (Nobody got in or out here, largely because Holster was taking some port.) Then they came to another wayside station where the third man got out without speaking. When they came to another wayside station, the man with the snake said . . .

Well, the story must be broken off—owing to lack of paper and wayside stations. Lieut. Holster is now at the Staff College (wayside station—Camberley). The Mess occasionally gets further bits of the story, and there was a rumour (in 1937 it was) that one of the men had said, during a halt at a wayside station, that his snake was imaginary, but this has not been verified to date. Of course during the wine-tasting he was stopped long before that part; but the port, which was the light port, Cherry & Co.'s 'Tawny No. 1', was approved by the Mess and called 'Mongoose'.

Feeling that to taste port properly one should try all samples consecutively, if not simultaneously, the next bottle was immediately opened. The sound of the cork brought Second Lieut. Swordfrog in from the billiard-room, thinking some one had called him. As he had been playing snooker, he had his cue with him. Taking his cue he at once co-opted himself on to the Wine Committee.

Not being able to un-opt him the rest of the Committee were forced to give him a glass. He drank it, and owing to an oversight on the part of Lieut. Bayonet—who has never been caught like that since—drank Lieut. Bayonet's as well, and owing to an oversight on the part of Major Saddle-flap—who was looking out of the window to see if the rain was stopping—drank his as well. Finding that Lieut. James had by then hastily swallowed his own glass and buttoned the remainder of the bottle into his tunic, he was forced from lack of material to return to the billiard-room. Here he went straight to the table and having successfully volunteered the pink four times running, finally proceeded to put down the green, blue, pink, and black in rapid succession. Whereupon the port, Cherry & Co.'s 'Two Crowns', was called 'Snooker'.

The third name, 'King Beaver', is a little difficult to explain. Various theories have been put forward by the survivors of the day, but no one has any tenable theory as to how or why the word 'Beaver' got into the name at all. The word 'King' is attributed by Lieut. James (Lieut. Bayonet concurring) to the fact that El Rei came somewhere into the name of the port, and the word 'Rei' may originally have had something to do with Portuguese Royalty. Or again may not. Anyway, an empty bottle of Cherry & Co.'s 'El Rei' port ultimately emerged from a haze of mystery christened 'King Beaver'.

It was then proposed by Lieut. Holster that the three original members of the Committee should present silver decanter labels with these names upon them to the Mess. The motion was carried unanimously, owing largely to Lieut. Bayonet not hearing quite what the motion was, Major Saddle-flap looking out of the window again, and Lieut. James being asleep. Lieut. James was woken up and deputed to arrange for their purchase, which he effected through an uncle of his at 12/6d. each, a bill for 48/6d. (three times 12/6d.) being subsequently but unsuccessfully presented to the others by Lieut. *'Honest'* James, who explained that he thought it just worth trying, anyway!

So next time you dine in our Mess bring this with you and don't ask questions.

FLICK-SHOOTING

WHAT with the continual calling up of the various classes for war service, our battalion has been flooded out with young men who have to be made into soldiers as soon as possible. They start by Turning to the Right by Numbers and end up as an Expeditionary Force. Somewhere in between they have a perfect orgy of musketry. Our first batch are already hard at work on range practice, and Captain Bayonet has been heard to say they're getting on so well, they'll shoot somebody one of these days. There is in fact Somebody they all want to shoot.

Yesterday, however, owing to rain they didn't go to the ranges; instead they had what turned out to be one of the happiest afternoons the camp has ever known.

It was the new 'Cinematograph Weapon-Training Target'. We'd never seen one before, but now every one is living for the next time we're allowed a go at it. Flick-shooting, we call it.

To explain it briefly, the target, at the end of a twenty-yard indoor range, is a special film screen of two thicknesses of stiff paper with an iron plate a couple of feet farther back. From behind and above the firing-point a projector throws pictures on to the screen, these pictures being films of actual operations, infantry attacks and so on. The troops, using small-bore rifles, then fire at targets which are indicated by their commander in the usual manner. ('Range, three 'undred—two fingers left of funny-looking tree by 'ouse—advancin' 'ostile patrol—two rounds rapid—fire!')

The impact of the bullets on the iron plate at the back actuates a spring which stops the picture for a second, and also switches on lights behind, to illuminate the holes just made in the paper screens. The commander then comments on the result, also in the usual manner. ('Lousy! Wot the 'ell d'you think you're firing at? Skylarks?') On restarting, one of the paper sheets is mechanically given a slight side movement which closes the holes, and off one goes again.

The troops found the whole thing quite delightful. To wipe out a patrol and then with your last round to pick off an irrelevant cow grazing at the side of the picture was far better than ping-pong balls at a shooting gallery. ('Nah then, 'oo fired at that cow?' 'Beg pard'n, I thought it was the corporal in charge!') Or one could snipe at a solitary scout and actually see the bullet-hole in the air some inches from his head. ('Bet it gave 'im a fright, anyway.') While to watch an attack rise up from a trench and then to wither it with fire till the picture stopped for thirty seconds on end and the hostile line, riddled with bullet-holes, looked like Brighton Pier at night, gave one a splendid feeling of triumphant power. Unfortunately this triumph was a little dashed when, on the picture restarting, the line continued to advance without a single casualty. ('Too bad, chum, you must be using blank!' 'No, they're holding up the dead 'uns, like in Boh Jest.' 'Well, 'ere they come, anyway—'adn't we better fix bayonets, corp?')

By the time the short film had been round twice ('Hey, corp, this is where we came in!') the troops had got to recognize details. They were now ready for the sergeant who for a brief second looked out of a tank and had him every time. They were also ready for the man who in one attack accidentally stumbled and fell; at the appropriate moment he was hit by half a dozen shots and next second realistically down he went. There was also the officer who bent over to pick up a map. . . .

After a while Captain Bayonet went up to the projection-room to ask whether there wasn't another film. There wasn't, but Corporal Foresight in charge there, looking very deliberately at a point over Bayonet's right shoulder, mentioned that he *did* have by him the films which had been shown in the camp movie-theatre last week and hadn't gone back yet. Bayonet hesitated, looked guiltily round, and at last caught Foresight's eye in a conspiratorial manner. . . . 'Well, just a—a selected reel or so,' he said. 'Good practice for them!' he added hastily.

There never has been, or will be, another afternoon like that. Bayonet stayed up in the projection-room to watch, and the troops thought he'd gone. Indeed, one of them was heard saying so—'Old Beenut's pushed off for 'is tea.' 'Tea! Orficers don't 'ave tea; they 'as whiskies and sodahs.' The amused Bayonet could make out Foresight's neck reddening in vicarious apology as he put on the first reel.

It was some sort of high-life story and a dinner-party was in progress. The troops thus had plenty of practice shooting at bottles, glasses, table decorations, butlers, and so on. ('Range, one 'undred—at that bloke's fizz—one round—fire!' At which the champagne glass lit up with bubbles such as Dom Perignon could never have visualized.) Then they got on to more difficult targets: hitting a mouthful of fish poised on a fork before it disappears like a rabbit into a hole is tricky work. ('From that shirt-front—two fingers left—bit o' mutton—fire!') Finally they started a wholesale massacre of the diners—'all except Myrna Loy, boys'—and Bayonet had the reel changed.

The new one concerned some sort of dishonourable attack by the villain later in the evening. The sound mechanism naturally wasn't functioning, but the troops supplied the words. Or rather it was soon left to one expert who had evidently studied ventriloquism in civilian life. 'What-ho! A nice little bit of goods!' began the sauve, white-waistcoated villain, entering the heroine's room. To which she retorted in a spirited falsetto: 'Go outside again and knock, you dirty-nosed skunk!' In spite of severe shooting in the stomach the villain, however, stood his ground, and a little later on was struggling fiercely with the girl to the accompaniment of incongruous baby-talk and

95

bullets: 'Won't-ums little ootsy-tootsy let popsy-wopsy kissums?' 'Kiss my foot!' replied the damsel. 'You'll get a sock in the pan in a minute!' It turned out to be a bullet in the jaw, but it was near enough. 'Where's my blasted boy-friend?' continued the lady, on which cue the hero entered and under normal circumstances would have fallen upon the villain—except that as he paused in the doorway he was neatly sniped in the right eye. 'Shame!' cried the troops, and the delinquent had to excuse himself by saying he never did really care for Tyrone Power.

When the young lady's conversation became really too luridly barrack-room, Bayonet put on another reel. This ended the entertainment. For it was a news-reel and happened to show Hitler in mid-speech. . . .

All the ammunition went in one and a quarter minutes, and Bayonet hurriedly appeared and fell the troops in outside, just as they were going in to finish off with their bayonets.

REVENGE IN THE WAR OFFICE

'WHAT a —— *dear* chap!' said Lieutenant Swordfrog feelingly, as the door closed behind a certain Major Folder.

'*Ever* so sweet!' Capt. Abeyance relaxed in his chair—as far as one can relax in a chair in the War Office. 'We just love him, don't we?' he added to Captain Intray at the other desk.

Intray merely made a vulgar noise. There was no real affection in it.

Our Lieutenant Swordfrog was up in town for the day on what he called duty connected with the war. This meant half an hour in Room XQ2 at the Battle Shack, a heavy lunch at his club, the latest 'flick' in the afternoon, the latest girl-friend to cocktails, and a return to the Mess at Havershot in the evening, brushing sweat from his brow and saying he wished the war was over and Army officers could get back to normal peace-time duties instead of All This Work.

In Room XQ2, however, he had just witnessed a distressing scene. A certain new-made Major from another department had rushed in and thrown his weight about in an offensive and officious manner at two brother officers.

'You wouldn't think,' continued Abeyance, 'that he's only been in the Army two months.'

'Is he always like that?' asked Swordfrog.

'Generally. Of course we—er—have our own little way of getting even.'

'What can you do?'

'Shall we show him, Intray?'

'Well, Folder's certainly earned it to-day.'

'Right!' Abeyance picked up the telephone while Intray went to the window and announced: 'It's O.K. It's there.'

'Give me Major Folder's office, please. . . . 'Ullo!' His voice suddenly changed to one polite, official, but firm, and Swordfrog pricked up his ears. 'Excuse me, sir, is that a Major Folder? . . . This is Inspector Daniells of Scotland Yard speaking. I've information that you're the owner of a grey saloon car ALD 494. Is that correct?' By now Swordfrog could almost see the neat serge suit and the bowler hat. 'Now, sir, that car has been parked outside in the public streets since 9.20 a.m., over two hours . . . Yes, sir, *I* know it's war-time and it's doing no 'arm, but it's obstructing, if you get my meaning. . . . Yes, sir, *I* know, but you can get a summons for that. . . .'

'He's spluttering more this morning,' remarked Intray judicially, listening close at hand. 'Probably got his typist in with him.'

'Now, now, now!' cut in Abeyance, patiently, soothingly. 'That sort of thing don't do no good, Major. Besides, I 'ear from the uniformed men that it's not the first time. . . . It's the law of the land, and after all I've got my duty to do. You give orders and expect them to be carried out, Major, don't you? Well, I . . . Yes, sir, they're always sorry afterwards, but it don't stop them doing it. . . . It'll 'ave to be a summons I'm afraid, Major. . . .'

'*Now* we're getting to it.' Intray nudged the enthralled Swordfrog.

Abeyance was grinning wickedly. 'Well, that's a very 'andsome apology indeed. I tell you what, Major; we'll overlook the car having been there over two hours, if you'll pop down and drive it round the building and then park it again, sir. That'll mean you've only just come, if you take my meaning. . . . Not at all, sir. . . . We all try to 'elp in these times. But you won't leave it too long again, will you? After all, orders is orders, as the saying is. . . . Good day, Major.'

Abeyance hung up. The awed Swordfrog nearly applauded.

'He was Detective Sergeant Simmons last time,' explained Intray. 'Drops a few more aitches and puts in a few more "Major's".'

'To think of that fellow,' began Swordfrog, giggling, 'rushing down and getting . . .'

'Oh, we don't need to *think* only. Come on!' Abeyance led the way to the window. 'That's the car, the grey one. . . . Ah, there he is!'

Unconscious of his delighted gallery, the tubby, uniformed figure of Major Folder was scuttling across the pavement below. He got in his car and at once had trouble with two others parked ahead and astern, eventually scratching one of their wings. He looked furtively round; his neck, even at that distance, was seen to grow visibly redder.

'Quite up to form,' approved Abeyance. 'Only last Tuesday he got his rear bumper hooked up and had to have three messengers out to help. That was *well* worth the money. . . . Ah, he's off!'

The car shot out into the traffic and round the corner. In a little while it reappeared. Swordfrog heard a click from a stop-watch. 'Tut! Tut!' said Intray. 'Four minutes thirty-two. That's bad! He must have run over some one on the other side.' He wrote the figure on a wall chart, which Swordfrog saw already had several entries, and an accompanying graph.

'His best time was two fifty-five,' said Abeyance proudly, 'but that was when I was an Assistant Commissioner and fairly well slammed it into him. . . . Quick! Come on with us and you'll see the last act! It's always good!'

Snatching up an important-looking file each, and followed by Swordfrog, almost helpless with laughter, the two dashed down to the ground floor.

Flushed, angry and heated, Major Folder was just coming in. No one was more surprised to meet him than Captain Abeyance.

'Ah! hullo, sir!' He then raised a significant eyebrow at Intray and looked at his watch. 'Eleven thirty-five,' he murmured. 'Bit early, of course; still, I suppose they're just open.'

Intray looked wistful. 'I'd love to slip out and have one but *I* can't spare the time. Got too much work to do.'

Shaking their heads sadly they passed rapidly on.

LIEUTENANT HOLSTER'S PROMOTION

THE fact that we have been at war for some months does not, I am glad to say, militate against our having a little joke now and then. And not only us, but even the 'higher-ups', it seems, are not above sparing a few minutes to keep a good jest going.

It all began with a very simple misprint—just a figure 'o' in mistake for a '9'—but the result was that our Lieutenant Holster's promotion to Captain was published to the world by the *London Gazette* as with effect from Dec. 2nd. 1039.

No one noticed the error for some time because the news was given verbally to the Mess breakfast-table by Captain Bayonet, who had bagged the *Times* first, and he only read as far as 'Lt. R. Holster to be Capt. . . .' before breaking off to remark loudly that the war must be going pretty badly for us, if they had to let old 'Gatbag' hoist a third wart. He then disappeared to warn the Mess Secretary that, in view of information received, he had every reason to suppose that there would be a big rush order for fizz at Mess that night, and he'd better start a new page on Holster's Wine Account.

The great event having been expected for some time and the news now being common property, no one thought to look at the *Gazette* again till that

evening, when Holster himself, in the midst of pre-
dinner sherry, had a sudden moment of sheer
panic. He had just recollected that free champagne under false pretences might easily be the
Mess's idea of a good practical joke, and so he flew
to the paper for reliable confirmation before the
first cork should pop. . . .

The discovery of the misprint, which technically
made Holster the senior captain in the whole
British Army, opened up quite a new field. Swordfrog said that after nine hundred years of holding
the rank he ought to be about due for Major, and
James kept asking him how his company had
done at Blenheim, but it was Bayonet who ultimately suggested that he ought to claim for all
his back pay.

Some hours later, when the evening had considerably broadened out, Holster actually sat down
in the midst of an admiring circle and wrote a
specimen letter beginning, 'Sir, I have the honour
to request . . .' embodying his grievance, and
ending with a demand to be paid some incredible
sum in arrears of pay at compound interest since
date of promotion to Captain early in 1039, *vide
London Gazette* of yesterday's date.

We all thought it quite funny at the time, but
perhaps we were wrong. Certainly Holster was
wrong when he believed that before retiring he had
destroyed the letter.

.   .   .   .   .   .

Some months later Holster's uncle, an important

bird in the War Office, met him in town and said, *'You've* got a nerve, my lad, writing like that! In war-time, too! 'Pon my soul, you might have been court-martialled!'

Well, you can guess at once what had happened —that some one, we never actually found out who, had found that letter and sent it up to the War Office—but it took Holster half an hour to realize, and even longer to recover. When, however, he feebly asked if he ought to write and apologize, murmuring something about youthful ebullition of spirits, the uncle said indignantly: 'Certainly not: it's the best joke we've had for years. Why, it's started a complete War Office File. As a matter of fact it's just been passed to me in connexion with some point or other, but . . .' he broke off, 'better come along and see it.'

In the War Box the uncle unlocked an enormous safe in his room, and after first handing Holster by mistake a terribly important-looking document marked Secret at every pore and headed 'EXTRACTS FROM LETTERS RECEIVED FROM SOLDIERS' WIVES ABOUT PENSIONS', and then hurriedly taking it away in some confusion, finally produced a large file topped by Holster's letter.

It seemed that there were few departments of the Battle Shack that it hadn't been to, growing in stature as it went. The branch dealing with officers' pay had naturally had it first, and in a long Minute they had analysed the claim, pointed out among other things that the rate of interest

demanded was wrong, particularly in the Plan-
tagenet era, and so had recalculated the claim.
This, while still leaving an incredible total, resulted,
of course—the Finance Branch being what it is—
in a big reduction.

A little later the Transport people seemed to
have got it, in view of the large delivery of bullion,
for it had been pointed out by some one else that
no banking system could cope with the figures,
their columns being little more than an inch in
width. After excursions into other departments
over the question of armed guards for specie, the
difficulty of obtaining transport in war-time, and
the effect of heavily laden lorries on the roads
leading to the barracks where the officer concerned
was stationed, it found its way to the medical
branch. Here opinion was strongly averse to
repaying so much money to a junior officer in one
sum, in view of the effect on the brain. There
were several interesting pages about this, including
a digressive report from some one in authority at
the Royal Military Looney Bin. It was eventually
suggested that the delivery of one small hand-cart
of gold three times a day after meals for a week
would be the utmost that would be consistent with
the recipient's mental stability, and suggested that
arrangements might be made for part payment of
the rest in kind. It was thus it got to Holster's
uncle, who had to do with Stores.

'I am just completing a Minute on it,' he said,
'and I think the affair can now be settled up.
You see, I've discovered that after the battle of

Bannockburn there were serious defalcations in Army stores. You were only a junior officer of some three hundred years' seniority at the time, but you are now the senior officer surviving of those responsible. So we are working out a claim, and strangely enough it almost balances with your claim for back pay. To be accurate, it comes out slightly in our favour, as you still owe us for "Bows, long, military, yew, without string . . . 1", but if you are at your Club at six o'clock to-night I can accept payment in kind—say a couple of Five-Rounds-Rapid cocktails.'

All very reprehensible in times of stress—but let's call it Much Needed Relaxation from War Strain.

SECOND LIEUTENANT O'HOOLIGAN

WE shall be glad when Second Lieutenant O'Hooligan leaves us for the front, wherever the front may be at the time. We shall also be a little sorry for any Germans he runs up against. We admit they have to be taught a lesson, but loosing O'Hooligan on them seems a little drastic. Machine-gunning and dive-bombing and so on, yes, but O'Hooligan—we-ell, it's not as though they've destroyed Buckingham Palace yet. . . .

For O'Hooligan is forty, six-foot-two, very broad, very Irish, and tough as teak. He has sailed over half the world, tramped over the other half, and apparently rough-housed over all of it. His joining our depot Mess was something like having a Stokes bomb dropped through a skylight. We're fairly light-hearted and given to a spot of ragging about after dinner—at least the younger ones, now back from France, are—but O'Hooligan's idea of fun and games made even the liveliest of them look like a grey-beard pottering about in the sun after a six-months' convalescence.

O'Hooligan celebrated his arrival that first evening in a mild way and the casualties were five glasses, a plate, a picture of Lord Kitchener, and a twisted ankle for Lieutenant Holster. He'd just been teaching us an energetic little parlour game he'd picked up in New York's Bowery.

The next night he warmed up. We played what he called Bangalore polo with spoons, chairs, and a heavy round stone match-stand weighing several pounds. It was supposed to stay on the floor, but O'Hooligan twice knocked the back out of a chair with it and ended by driving it at the height of five-foot-six through a three-ply black-out screen and the window behind. We know the height, because Lieutenant Swordfrog was standing near the window and proved by a nasty graze across the forehead that he didn't strike only on the box.

The third night O'Hooligan organized some 'Try Your Strength' contests—he said he and some students used to amuse themselves with them when he was living in Cologne—but the German furniture must have been much more solidly made than ours. The Adjutant got a black eye at one point during the evening and Major Saddleflap's strength broke a picture of Wellington.

In spite of all this we couldn't help liking the fellow; and even the Colonel fell under his spell when on the fourth night O'Hooligan cracked a walnut for him by putting it on the table and banging it once with his forehead. The walnut, of course, couldn't be eaten afterwards: it had to be swept away with a crumb brush. A fellow in a Singapore dive had taught him, he explained; he'd also taught him a little game with piled chairs, called 'First up Everest', which he'd now show us, and which was reasonably exciting. It was. O'Hooligan's games would have been considered exciting even in a bayonet charge.

Most remarkable of all, O'Hooligan managed all this on an astonishingly small amount of drink. No doubt his Irish temperament just fermented inside him and did the rest. We shuddered, though, to imagine the evening when he should take one more than usual.

As a matter of fact it came the following night, when we had our weekly 'guest-night'. On these occasions the dinners are generally a little better, and the fun a little faster by way of entertainment for our guests.

We first became apprehensive when O'Hooligan took a second glass of port and announced with a wildish look in his eye that he had quite a new game to teach us that night, but it might possibly be a little rough. The guests, who didn't know him, clamoured for it, but we managed to keep him occupied for some while, trying to crack a walnut in his usual manner. Actually it was a cast-iron one we had made and painted for the purpose, hoping he'd lay himself out, but he only seemed to get more and more annoyed at his failure, and acquired a bruise on his forehead about the same size as the walnut. Eventually the Colonel stopped him because it was splintering the table.

Then the game started. How it went I don't quite remember. All I know is that half-way through O'Hooligan broke somebody's arm, and the whole party stopped. He was terribly contrite, but all the while we felt that at the back of his mind he was thinking that weaklings who couldn't play a simple parlour game without falling to pieces ought to be in a girls' school. Why, it had just come apart in his hand like that . . .

The accident stopped any games for a week, but we missed them. Moreover, we'd never liked the owner of the broken arm, anyway. So next guest-night we started once more.

About half-way through we began to notice that same wild look in O'Hooligan's eye. It seemed to indicate that, all in the spirit of the utmost cama-raderie, of course, someone would be in hospital before morning. The Adjutant, whose black eye had just got better, suggested that we all played poker instead, but there was no stopping O'Hooligan once he got going.

At last Captain Bayonet sneaked round to the back of the Mess and smuggled in a pick-helve, which he hid behind the door. We then asked O'Hooligan again to stop, but he refused. Under some pretext, therefore, three of us backed him up towards the door and Bayonet, unobserved, beaned him from behind with the helve. A pick-helve is three foot long and about three inches in diameter, and all the glasses on the mantelpiece rang at the impact.

Knowing O'Hooligan we almost expected him merely to rub his head fretfully and go on talking, but he heeled over like a dynamited chimney and we put him to bed.

Next morning we huddled together at one end of the breakfast-table for protection when O'Hooligan came in. We anticipated bloodthirsty threats, if not instant massacre.

Instead he beamed wanly at us. 'An' how are all you fellows this foine morning? Be gosh but we had a good night last night, didn't we? I think I must have drink taken the merest trifle, for I cannot remember a thing that happened at the latter end; an' I have a head on me like a concrete pill-box. . . .'

We all broke out into friendly talk, but no one told him. . For it had given us the clue.

Each guest-night now the pick-helve is hidden behind the door, and when O'Hooligan looks like getting really dangerous it comes unobtrusively into play, Bayonet being our official striker-out. O'Hooligan is then carried off with a beatific smile on his face, to wake next morning to the memory of a night so grand it's nearly all a blank.

Still, we'll be glad when he does go off to the front, even though, as I say, we feel we ought to warn the Germans—or at any rate send a note to them, suggesting they include pick-helves in their armament, as well as tanks.

LIEUT. SPANNER DEFEATS DEMOCRACY

WE are admittedly fighting for the preservation of democracy. When therefore one comes across little portions of it preserved as beautifully as flies in aspic, as permanently as quails in amber, it gives one quite a sense of achievement. It is indeed gratifying to realize, for instance, that after fifteen months of war several Government departments can still spend more time over shuffling the responsibility for doing a small job on to one another than it would take any one of them to do the darn thing.

Lieutenant Spanner is the hero of this particular story. At the time he was in charge of a big building in the South of England in which were several machines busily printing maps. (For no ascertainable reason this particular job came under the Ministry of Agriculture and Fisheries. Don't ask *me* why!) The building was new and large and white, but it was not till one day he found Corporal Gadget laboriously stripe-painting a sentry-box just outside it for fear of "ostile observances, sir, so giving away the position of our printing shop,' that it occurred to him that it would be more effective perhaps to have the building itself camouflaged. So he wrote to the Ministry of Food and Fish, and there the matter should have ended.

But thank heaven for the spirit of democratic England, it didn't. It merely began.

The Ministry wrote back by return—well, say within two weeks—and said that the actual building belonged to the Office of Works: it was their responsibility, not ours . . . frightfully sorry and all that. So Spanner wrote the Office of Works. The O. of W., a cagey lot at the best of times, realized at once that, if they weren't pretty careful, they might actually have to do the job. By way of exploring avenues of escape they tentatively asked, for a start, what was in the building. They were of course prepared to go on asking questions for weeks in the hope of getting a cue for an exit line, but they drew lucky right away, for the reply naturally was: 'Printing machines.' Delightedly they said: 'Ah, but that's the business of His Majesty's Stationery Office,' and returned with a happy sigh to their normal work—whatever the hell that is!

The Stationery Office, however, were also old hands at the game. They said in effect: 'Printing machines? Nothing to do with us. *We* do all *our* printing.' So back Spanner wrote to the Office of Works who, still prepared to leave no stone unturned to avoid having to *do* anything, were now luckily inspired to ask what the devil the printing machines *were* printing there?

Restraining an impulse—for several weeks had passed and Spanner was getting impatient—to reply, 'Counterfeit pound notes', he wrote back, 'Military maps', whereupon the Office of Works, beaming all over its face, was able to reply that it would appear that such fell within the purview of the War Office, who undoubtedly would accept responsibility for camouflaging the building in which their maps were printed: indeed, if properly handled, they might even go so far as actually to have it done, though perhaps that was taking rather too rosy a view of the situation.

Wearily Spanner wrote to the War Office. The War Office, being naturally busy with a war, hadn't time for landscape work. They said curtly that it was the business of the Ministry under which Lieutenant Spanner's work fell. He should apply to the Ministry of Food and Fish.

Thus in a bare two months the wheel had turned full circle. A lesser man might have left it there and either resigned his commission, or gone down to the local to get drunk, or shot himself. Or even all three. Or he might have scrounged the paint, done it himself, and got court-martialled for exceeding his duty. Spanner, however, did none of these things. He remembered that quite a number of his maps were supplied to and used by the Air Force, who, with the Navy and the Wigan Town Council, were about the only people of importance who hadn't yet been dragged into the business.

So he wrote to the Air Ministry, who replied in due course (ten days) that they were hurt, amazed, and indeed rather outraged at the suggestion that they should undertake the responsibility of camouflaging a whole large building belonging to some one else, just because they happened to have used a few maps printed therein. Spanner, they said, with the misguided idea of being helpful, should apply to the Ministry of Food and Fish.

Spanner thereupon played his last card. He remembered how his uncle, a celebrated back-bencher, had told him the only way to get any-thing done in a democracy was to take some one out to lunch. Quite frequently it didn't matter who, as long as the lunch was good: *something* in-variably resulted. There was a certain *je ne sais quoi* about a lunch, Spanner's uncle said, which started things working.

So Spanner mobilized his financial resources and then rang up the only friend he happened to have in the Air Ministry with a lunch invitation. The friend, having recovered from his surprise, accepted heartily, and made it the following day, apparently afraid lest Spanner should change his mind, or discover that he was confusing him with some one else.

Spanner lushed him up to the best that his Club and rationing could achieve, and then said that he'd been thinking of reporting something to the Air Ministry but didn't know whether it was im-portant enough. 'Tell us what it is, old man!' said the friend genially, from out of two bobs' worth of cigar-smoke, from above twelve bobs' worth of lunch, and from behind three bobs' worth of old brandy, 'I might be able to help, old man! Do anything I can for you, old man!'

Spanner thereupon explained that down his way he had noticed a large new white building which he rather suspected the German raiders were using as a landmark. It was undoubtedly clearly visible at night, and certainly he had observed that they always changed course when directly over it.

'Most important!' said the other, and added quickly, 'But don't bother to write to the Air Ministry! *I*'ll mention it in the right quarter.' For in spite of the free lunch he thought he might as well have what credit was going. 'It certainly *ought* to be camouflaged,' he repeated warmly. 'One thing, though: what about the people who own the place? Would they object, do you think, if we wanted to do it?'

Demurely Spanner replied that he thought they wouldn't mind, if tactfully approached.

The very next day an Air Ministry official descended on Spanner. He spoke round the subject for some while—the general effects of bombing, the way in which the Germans found their way, landmarks, and so on—and at last very diffidently pointed out that it was faintly possible the building under Spanner's care might be so used. Perhaps it would be as well to be on the safe side—'camouflage it, you know; of course, we'd do it ourselves,' he added hastily.

Spanner hummed and hawed. He had no authority to give permission. The building was very nice and bright as it was. He rather liked the effect himself. He might get into trouble. He must think it over. . . .

It was then twelve-thirty and the Air Ministry official, under the impression he was a mine of low cunning, said: 'Perhaps you'd come out to lunch with me and we'll discuss it further?'

This, of course, was all that Spanner had been waiting for, because he didn't see why he should be down a lunch in doing some one else's work for them.

He ate and drank to as near his original outlay as possible, and finally he was persuaded, over the final three bobs' worth of old brandy, to let the Air Ministry camouflage his map-printing building. The fellow told him he'd really been very decent about it and he wished more people would see things in the proper way.

But the whole thing has heartened Spanner considerably. And indeed all of us. Democracy cannot perish from this earth. . . .

OUR P.A.D. TEST

P.A.D., or Passive Air Defence, is the Army equivalent of A.R.P. P.A.D. is largely What To Do When The Bombs Fall—in contrast to the more active Shoot The Bomber Down Before He Does It, or R.A.F. In the camp where our battalion now is, P.A.D. consists principally of two large centrally-situated water-tanks, and a brand-new and powerful fire-engine. Should the camp receive a bomb, these two are supposed to get together and passively defend us.

'The point is, though,' said our Colonel Howitzer to the Adjutant soon after our arrival, 'how long are those tanks good for?'

The Adjutant hadn't the vaguest idea and so replied briskly: 'They're pretty big, sir, and always full to the top. And all the rain-pipes from the near-by buildings lead into them. So . . .'

'Yes, yes, yes,' snapped Howitzer. 'But suppose we empty them before the fire's out, what are you suggesting we do? Pray for rain?'

'But they hold any amount of water, sir. . . .'

'And that fire-engine *throws* any amount of water. *I* want to know how long they're *good* for! Here! It's perfectly simple. Let a, b, and c be the dimensions of a tank, then a times b times c is the number of cubic feet of water. . . . And if a cubic foot of water weighs x pounds . . . And y

pounds is the weight of a gallon . . . And—er—mm—mm . . . It's *perfectly* simple!' he repeated defiantly, after scribbling a while on the blotting-paper. 'It's just a matter of *a*, *b*, *c*, *x*, and *y*.'

'And *z*, sir. The number of gallons per hour the fire-engine throws.'

'Eh? . . . Oh, that makes it even simpler.' He figured a little longer, then threw his pencil down angrily. '*I* can't be bothered with these details. Get those three new young officers on it. Good brain exercise! Tell 'em to find out all the data and work it out.'

So our three new subalterns were set to work, and after a while they reported results. Unfortunately they did not agree. One made it seven hours and a quarter, one two hours, fourteen minutes, and ten-point-eight-six-recurring seconds, while Second Lieutenant Tunic merely stated that in his opinion the water would outlast any fire the camp could possibly have.

Colonel Howitzer, temporarily fascinated by the ten-point-eight-six-recurring seconds, forgot to be angry. He only said: 'Well, as they can't agree, we'll solve the problem practically. Empty the tanks with the fire-engine and time the operation!'

'Emptying *one* tank only, sir, will do,' suggested the Adjutant tactfully; 'they're the same size. And we don't want an air-raid to come and catch us—er—still praying for rain.'

'Of course. When I say *tanks* I naturally mean only *one* tank, and multiply the answer by two. Emptying both would be damned stupid!' He glared at the Adjutant. You can't beat our Colonel Howitzer.

Two afternoons later the R.S.M., with an air of one dissociating himself from a rather childish business, paraded the fire picquet and the engine. A crowd of men off duty collected to see the fun. The suction hose was plunged in one of the brimming tanks. Two men held the nozzle. The Adjutant said 'Ready, sir!', Colonel Howitzer, at grips with a large stop-watch, shouted 'Go!' And off we went.

The first thing we found was that the innocent-looking hose had a powerful hidden personality. It was one of those hoses that, when in action, take far more than two men to hold the nozzle. In harmony, however, with the practical rather than theoretical nature of the whole test, Privates Pullthrough and Sling, the two men concerned, only discovered this fact by trial and error, one of each being quite enough.

The first pulse of the jet lifted them off their feet, the second, shooting out a sudden loop in the hose just behind the nozzle, took Private Sling on the solar-plexus, and the third caught him under the chin, as he simultaneously released the hose and all his breath, and knocked him cold. Whereupon the fourth and subsequent pulsations simply played merry hell with the overmatched Private Pullthrough who, taking the thing as a direct challenge to his manhood, continued to cling on. It waved him about like a rag on the end of a stick; it hammered him up and down; it wiped the floor with him; it wiped the side of an adjacent barrack hut with him; finally, like a horse flicking froth from its nose, it flirted him off, up, and, parabolically, into the water tank. Slightly calmer, it then merely writhed about on the ground, a razor-edged jet sweeping the feet from under every one in an arc of thirty degrees, till the R.S.M. stopped the engine pumping.

Colonel Howitzer decided not to count that bit in the test—largely because in the excitement of dodging, he had clicked his stop-watch back to the start. 'Only a few gallons gone. Makes no difference,' he said airily. Neither of these views was shared by those men who'd been in the direct line of fire.

For the next round the R.S.M. detailed four of the huskiest troops he could find. They advanced purposefully on the hose with the air of men about to tackle a fighting anaconda. In this attitude Private Sling, slowly recovering consciousness, heartily concurred: it was not for some days that he could get rid of the impression that he *had* tackled a fighting anaconda.

The huskies seized the hose. The Colonel roared 'Go!' and off we went again. This time they held the thing, though now and then they were fluttered about like the tail of a kite, as the anaconda tried to wrest itself free. The fire-engine continued to pump: the water gushed out.

New trouble soon arose, this time over the disposal of the water. Colonel Howitzer had cheerfully said: 'Play it on the ground! It'll find its way to the drains.' Unfortunately it seemed a stranger in those parts and the few drains it did find pretty soon gave up the struggle. They could deal with a couple of cloud-bursts or so, but not this. The Colonel, however, in full blast with his watch, was not going to stop the test, and soon the jet of water was being switched feverishly to any place that wasn't actually a foot under water, and the camp looked as though it were afloat.

An attempt to play the stream harmlessly on the roof of a hut—harmlessly, that is, except for two windows broken on the way up—was then tried and abandoned. Firstly, because the roof began to disintegrate under the impact, and secondly, because it was realized that it hardly helped the test, in that the water was running off the roof into the drain-pipes and so back to the tank.

A subsequent effort by the huskies to shoot it harmlessly in the air and let it fall to earth they knew not where, was also called off. Blasphemy from positions of shelter behind various huts pretty soon told them where it *had* fallen to earth; moreover those in hiding seemed to assume it was being done on purpose and looked like making an ugly rush to capture the nozzle. And when the Adjutant suddenly realized that the jet was going perilously near the grid high-voltage cables overhead, with the death of the huskies by electrocution imminent, he had it lowered to earth, with another window as casualty, and tentatively suggested that the Colonel had better call the test off.

Howitzer, however, was adamant. He continued to be adamant, even when the discovery that the water was being lowered simultaneously in both tanks showed that they were not unnaturally interconnected by an underground pipe.' We'll just halve the answer, then,' he said masterfully, but confusedly, 'before we double it.'

Half an hour went by and water was everywhere. The level of the tanks had been reduced by a foot —but there for a further half-hour it unaccountably stayed. The exhausted hose-party was relieved. Another half-hour went by. The water stayed at the same level. Howitzer was definitely puzzled; and Corporal Foresight was heard suggesting that his stop-watch had stopped. Pumping went on. The water-level in the camp continued to rise, but that in the tanks remained stationary.

About the time when kit started floating out of the huts and Private Muzzle, 'B' Company humorist, was being surreptitiously funny with a pair of water-wings and a divining-rod, Second Lieutenant Tunic timidly approached the Adjutant.

'Are you—is the C.O. trying to *empty* the tanks completely, sir?'

'No, you young fool!' retorted the Adjutant between his teeth. 'He only wants a cupful for shaving.'

'Because, sir, I don't think he *can*. At least it'll take a very long time. You know you told us to find out all the data and that's why I said the water was sufficient for any fire. I mean, the C.O. can't empty the tanks till he's emptied the reservoir at Havershot. There's a long connecting-pipe which keeps the tanks full to a foot from the top—and rain-water only supplies the other foot—and so . . .'

The Adjutant, who saw himself having to tell the Colonel this, sprang to action. 'Find where the stop-cocks are and have them turned off at once!'

'Er—yes, sir. It'll still take time, though. They're at Havershot, twenty miles away. . . .'

It was at this point the R.S.M. took a hand. He was getting bored and wanted his tea. So he winked at Sergeant Grenade, in charge of the fire-engine, and a little later it faltered and stopped. Colonel Howitzer, on being told by Sergeant Grenade, apparently as puzzled as any one, 'that it might take an hour to get going, sir,' called the test off, announcing that he could work the result out from the figures he had got. 'Just a question of multiplying the time by x,' he said—and told young Tunic to do it.

THE EXPERT

GEORGE, who is in Military Intelligence in the War Office, told us about him. George came into the club one lunch-time, sank into a chair, loosened his Sam Browne, and called loudly for sherry. 'I have just had a morning with an Expert,' he announced. 'Gosh!'

'What kind? The Business Expert who tells you how to run the Army by City methods? Or the Mechanical Expert with a flying tank?'

No, this (said George, with reminiscent awe) was a Cipher Expert. One of those excessively brainy fellows—Professors of Higher Mathematics and so on in peace-time. Mind you, in their own line they're terrific. I mean, give them a cipher message that looks like the offspring of a scrambled alphabet and a lunatic's sum in trigonometry, and they'll skim it over as if it were merely a kid's Pat-had-a-rat book. But when it comes to ordinary things in an ordinary world they're rather at a loss. Indeed, I've heard of one chap who, having to multiply five by three, whipped out a slide-rule— they carry 'em around like fountain-pens—whizzed it back and forth a bit and announced, 'It's exactly fourteen point nine-nine-eight—oh, well, we'll call it fifteen: it's near enough!'

This particular Expert appeared suddenly in our room this morning. You won't believe a word of this, but it's all quite true. Indeed, if Spencer and I hadn't been previously warned to expect a representative from X21 at Millbank we might have put him down as a spy—except that no spy could look so eccentric. He had a gloriously vague look and wore enormous glasses like the headlamps of a racing car. His Sam Browne buckle was round on his left hip and his hair would have made a sergeant-major faint on the spot. It burst out all round from under his uniform cap like a dying chrysanthemum. The fact that he wore the cap with the front spring down in the packing position, just as it came from the box, didn't help the effect.

He looked dimly round the room, appeared for no ascertainable reason to decide that it was the wrong one, began to raise his cap politely with one hand, saluted instead with the other and started out of the door again. If Spencer hadn't called out, 'Who do you want to see?' and found that it was us all the time, he'd have drifted right out of our lives then and there. And would we have missed something?

Well, he came in, shut the door, opened it again, peered out, shut it once more and said: 'They told me it was very secret.' We now saw he had under his arm a locked brief-case attached to a chain, which he deposited carefully on the desk beside him as he sat down.

'I have come to bring you the new cipher code from X21. It's a double substitution with elimination of frequencies.' He launched into an enthusiastic spate of words, in the middle of which he suddenly put out a hand and made a sort of slow grasping or collecting motion in the air a little distance in front of his face. Instinctively Spencer and I looked at one another, we wondered if it were a secret sign to which we should reply in kind, but when he did it again a moment later we realized it was just an automatic gesture of his while talking. I don't think he knew he was making it, but it punctuated his subsequent conversation, and was exactly like a man gathering an apple off a tree. At least so I said, when discussing the point afterwards: Spencer maintained that they were peaches from the careful way he fingered them first.

We let him run down and then asked him what everything was about. He picked another apple and explained that he had to bring the document to us himself in person, as it was so very secret. 'Professor—I mean, *Captain* Chalmers was most emphatic. So I have it here with me.'

He got up very suddenly and walked over to the mantelpiece. The brief-case, which we now saw was chained to his belt, hesitated a moment and then jerked off the desk after him, together with my 'Out' tray, an inkpot, and several pencils. The Expert, turning from searching the mantelpiece, said happily: 'Ah, there it is!' and picked it up, together with the 'Out' tray's contents and the pencils. Personally I was busy wondering how on earth it had got into his mind that the case could possibly have been on the mantelpiece. It was chained to him and he hadn't been over to that part of the room. Then I had hurriedly to rescue the 'Out' tray papers, which he was putting away absently in his pockets. The pencils, beauties I'd been collecting for months, we never got. At the end of all this he picked another apple and sat down calmly. 'I have it in here,' he repeated, tapping the case.

'Right! I'll take it,' I said, but he only went on: 'You understand that it is very secret and important and mustn't be lost?'

Spencer replied gravely that we had fairly good arrangements for not losing secret things, so he could safely hand it over.

This sent him off on another tack, and after picking a couple more he told us that he had a method, too. A safe in the office with a combination. 'And,' he added triumphantly, as if it were the crowning master-stroke of organization, 'Professor Chalmers nearly always remembers the combination when I forget it.'

We liked the 'nearly always', but we were no nearer getting the document off him. 'You really have it with you?' we asked, feeling it was quite probable he'd left it behind in the safe. 'Of course,' he said, raising his eyebrows, and as he did so, believe it or not, the spring of his cap suddenly flipped up. It was most eerie. It was as if, instead of raising his eyebrows, he had raised his whole face. It was too much for us and we burst out laughing. He actually smiled wanly. 'It's always doing that,' he said, taking the cap off and pressing the spring down again. 'I can't get it to stay down properly.' We opened our mouths to explain and decided against it: it would be spoiling a good thing. He then got up suddenly and went to the window: we have a theory he thought it was a mirror and was going to see how his cap looked, but the brief-case took another plunge after him, this time with a bowl of paper-pins, and distracted his attention. We picked up the pins and he picked another apple—by now we had got to believe so much in this last that we could barely refrain from pointing out much riper ones—'See, on that bough there!'

'Could I have this document?' I said very firmly at last, and he began to fumble in his pockets.

'Isn't it in the case?' I suggested politely.

'Ah, yes,' he said, 'but there's the key, you know.' He produced stray cigarettes and the inevitable slide-rule and masses of papers, in one of which he became quite immersed, till we induced him to put it away.

'Funny thing,' he said at last, 'I seem to have mislaid the key. The case is locked up and chained to me,' he pointed out. 'For safety. But never mind,' he added brightly, 'there's always an answer to every problem.' And unbuckling his belt he took it off and presented us with the brief-case, chain and belt in one, and was about to take his departure when in a strangled voice Spencer pointed out that we still couldn't open the thing.

'Tut! How stupid! For the moment I was thinking it was the other key—the one for the chain. I think,' went on this incredible man, 'I must have left the case key behind.'

'Will you 'phone up your office in Millbank and ask them to send it round?'

'Certainly. Except'—here he picked a beauty from quite a high bough, a Cox's Orange, I believe —'I can't recollect the office number. I've got it on a slip of paper, but it's locked up in this brief-case. For safety.'

Spencer and I were now feeling like part of a Chinese puzzle—all those little boxes eternally inside one another. 'The exchange will get it,' said Spencer patiently, reaching for the receiver. 'X21, wasn't it?'

He raised his eyebrows—and cap. 'If you think one can mention it over the 'phone . . .' he said, struggling again with the spring. 'The safe combination, I mean,' he explained, 'because to tell the truth I recollect now I put the brief-case key in the safe after locking it up. I have a habit of putting everything in the safe because then I know where to find it.'

We just looked at one another. Finally I managed to speak. 'Couldn't you tell Captain Chalmers to get it out? He knows the combination too.'

'To be sure he does,' he replied, brightening. 'That'll solve everything, won't it?' He selected a rosy James Grieve—we almost expected to see him munch it—and started to read the papers on my desk upside down, leaving the whole thing to us.

Well, there was only one thing that could happen, and it did. The 'phone went before Spencer could ask for his call, and it was Captain Chalmers asking for 'Professor—er—Lieutenant Mead,' who might be in our office. Could Mead give him the combination of the safe, which unfortunately had slipped his memory.

Well, I know when I'm licked. I threw my hand in and told our Expert he'd better come again this afternoon. He looked relieved. I think even he was feeling the strain. He said good-bye and went. At the door we called him back and gave him his precious brief-case and belt, which he'd left on my desk. Not that it mattered: I bet the document wasn't in it after all. In his agitation he picked a cooker by mistake and bowed himself out with a last flip of his cap spring. When last seen he was vaguely trying to tie the chain round his waist and was carrying the belt. . . . Gosh!

But I swear Spencer's wrong. You don't get peaches growing as thick as that on the tree! . . .

'A' COMPANY AND THE FLY SITUATION

OUR battalion has at last received its formal invitation to attend the party being given by the French and Germans on the Continent, and great activity has naturally set in in our midst. I mean we have to be properly dressed for it and must travel light, which is why the Colonel, among other things, ordered a turn-out of the H.Q. shelves and cupboards and the destruction of all superfluous documents. The following file thus came into my hands and I hadn't the heart to destroy it. It dates from the time when we were in Palestine, helping to maintain law and order, and was tied up, symbolically enough, with lots of red tape.

Informal letter from Captain Bayonet, O.C. 'A' Company, 1st Loamshires (on detachment at Rigadoon), to Quartermaster (at H.Q. at Saraband).

Dear Ledger—There's too much nature out here in the wilds. In other words, my cooks report that the flies in the cookhouse are 'somethink crooel'; the troops have flies in all their quarters; and in fact Beelzebub is pretty busy. So here is an indent from my Q.M.S. Fourbytwo for fifty fly-papers, which please forward to whoever is responsible for supplying same and send the things out here at once for the love of Mike.   Yours,

                                             A. Bayonet.

Very formal letter from Capt. (Q.M.) Ledger to O.C. 'A' Company.

Sir—Reference your indent for Papers, Fly . . . 50, I am taking steps to obtain these and same will be sent you forthwith, when obtained, in due course.

G. Ledger,

Capt. (Q.M.)

PS.—I can trace no Private Beelzebub on your Company strength. I presume he is a local native employed as extra sanitary man. Well, you know that's quite unauthorized and you can't get no rations or kit for him, so don't try it on!

Memo from Q.M. to Someone-in-the-Ordnance.

Herewith indent for Papers, Fly . . . 50, please.

Answer to above.

Papers, Fly, are not an article of store here. Apply R.A.S.C.

Memo from Q.M. to Someone-in-the-R.A.S.C.

Herewith indent for Papers, Fly . . . 50, please.

Answer to above.

Don't keep 'em. Try Ordnance.

Telegram from Q.M. to Ordnance.

Papers fly fifty urgently required aaa please say how where to whom submit indent aaa urgent.

Letter from Ordnance to Q.M.

With reference to your telegram and further to

my earlier letter, I should have explained that while Papers, Fly, Complete, are not held in store here, we supply the viscid mucilage which is the adhesive constituent of the articles concerned. This will be issued on demand, but paper sheets to form the groundwork must be obtained from the R.A.S.C.

Phone message from Captain Bayonet to Q.M., taken down at H.Q. by Private Muzzle.

Sir—Capt. Bayonet 'phoned to say where the duce are his fly-papers please, and Behell Shebub is not a native but lord of flies see Bible.

Huffy Reply from Q.M. to O.C. 'A' Company.

Tell Capt. Bayonet the matter is in hand and not to bother me with talk about Bibles and such, even though we are in Palestine.

Formal Letter from Q.M., to Someone-in-the-R.A.S.C.

Sir—I am directed to apply to you for Sheets, Paper (Army Form Number not ascertainable), to form basis for Papers, Fly, urgently required by one of our Companies on detachment. Herewith, therefore, formal indent for Papers, Fly-paper, Without Viscid Mucilage, Sheets . . . 50.

G. Ledger,
Capt. (Q.M.)

Letter from R.A.S.C. to Q.M., 1st Loamshires.

No articles such as you mention, namely, 'Papers, Fly-paper, Without Viscid Mucilage,' exists officially. Suitable paper is, however, being sent you herewith.

10

Urgent Letter from Q.M. to R.A.S.C.

Ref. my QM/FP/14. Fifty sheets paper received, but please confirm that this is suitable paper for fly-paper. I understand the flies are very numerous, whereas the sheets sent won't accommodate more than two or three dozen flies at a time.

Answer from R.A.S.C. to Q.M.

Additional supply of paper is being sent in view of your complaint. Apply to Ordnance for instructions what to do with it.

Letter from Q.M. to Ordnance.

Sir—I am now in possession of a large supply of Paper, Fly-paper, Without Viscid Mucilage. Would you please supply Mucilage, Viscid, Fly-paper . . . 1 pint (or sufficient for three hundred sheets).

Letter from Ordnance to Q.M.

Herewith two and a half tundals of Mucilage (English equivalent 1·052 pints). Instructions for spreading on sheets follow.

Telegram from O.C. 'A' Company to Q.M.

Where hell my fly-papers. Beelzebub.

From Q.M. to O.C. 'A' Company.

Please find herewith:
   (1) Paper, Fly-paper for the purpose of, Sheets 300
   (2) Mucilage, Viscid, Fly-paper, Tundals 2½
   (3) Sheets, Instruction . . . 1

Letter from O.C. 'A' Company to Q.M.

Materials for fly-paper received, but only 128 sheets available, as owing to mucilage leaking rest are in one solid block. For same reason only about half a tundal mucilage is available, but Privates Pullthrough and Rifle are doing their best to make it go round by watering it down. Meanwhile please send further copy of instructions, sheet sent being embedded somewhere in the block of paper referred to above.

Letter from O.C. 'A' Company to Q.M.

Further to my yesterday's letter:

(i) Please send more paper, only 37 sheets being now available.

(ii) Please send any information available as to how to unstick various articles stuck together with mucilage, such as (*a*) Private Pullthrough's shorts and Orderly-room chair, (*b*) copy of Army Act and a portion of meat ration, (*c*) a mess tin, three handkerchiefs of Private Rifle's, and a photo of C.S.M. Magazine's wife, and (*d*) Private Sling's middle finger and thumb (luckily same hand).

(iii) Please send more mucilage.

Telegram from Q.M. to O.C. 'A' Company. (Dispatched before receipt of above.)

Ordnance state imperative not water down mucilage otherwise useless owing reduced viscidity stop in any case useless unless mixed with poison first as per instructions stop am applying medical officer for suitable poison stop suggest deferring manufacture fly-papers till this obtained.

Report from O.C. 'A' Company to Q.M. (crossing above).

(i) Four fly-papers, all that are now left, complete and in position by 9.0 a.m. this morning. Flies delighted with it and are turning up in larger numbers than we have yet seen. One or two of the smaller ones seem to find the going heavy, but in general they eat the mucilage off as soon as it is put on.

(ii) Ref. (ii) (*d*) of my previous letter, please now add little finger of other hand.

(iii) Please send more paper.

(iv) Please send more mucilage.

MR. SMITH

MR. SMITH is a lorry. Our Army is breaking away from the old traditions—dating back to the beginning of the war—of calling tanks, armoured vehicles, dragons, and lorries frivolous names like 'Boomps-a-Daisy', or 'Gert'. Our biggest concession to whimsicality is the name 'St. George' for our section's dragon.

Mr. Smith is more than an ordinary lorry. He is a scientific lorry. He was also for a brief period, when Lieutenant Spanner's engineering urge ran riot, an experimental lorry. You see, his job is to print battle maps. He actually carries a real map-printing press which occupies nearly the whole of his interior. In the remaining space are paper, ink, Sapper Satchell, and other map-printing requisites.

Mr. Smith touts for orders, so to speak, by going round divisional and corps H.Q., in their luxurious châteaux just outside French villages, for in one respect this war is much like the last. He arrives, plumps himself down in the courtyard with a sigh, and Lieutenant Spanner, R.E., at once goes in to report that everything is ready for hatching out a lovely clutch of whatever map the General has been sticking pins in that morning and now wants other people to play with too. After a day or so Mr. Smith has probably satisfied the General's map-urge, gathers himself up and patters off to fresh châteaux and Generals new.

Now it wasn't long before Lieutenant Spanner realized in a mood of research that there was a bad waste of energy going on, for Mr. Smith had one engine-thing—power-unit or prime-mover, if you want to go all sapper-hat—inside him to drive his printing machine, and another one outside to drive Mr. Smith. He said to Corporal Gadget: 'Why shouldn't we fix up Mr. Smith's own engine to do both jobs?'

'Be a saving-like, wouldn't it?' said Gadget, and Sapper Satchell, standing by, said 'Ar', very wisely. Satchell, by the way, was a pudding-faced man whose trade was that of 'machine-minder' and whose job it was to 'mind' the printing machine, supplying its wants by day and tucking it up at night.

'After all,' continued Spanner, 'we're always stationary when we're printing. . . .'

'And there's no call for to print when we're on the move,' finished Gadget, quite worked up about it.

'Ar!' endorsed Sapper Satchell, sucking his teeth.

'Then we'll get on the job this afternoon,' decided Spanner.

With great thoughts of promotion in the field for devotedly saving the Army the expense of one power-unit per map-printing lorry, Lieutenant Spanner and Corporal Gadget got to work, while Sapper Satchell buzzed gently about lending a hand. They disconnected the inside engine and laid it carefully in the courtyard, they fitted pulleys and bolts, they ran wires all over the place like a spider's web, and finally they set about installing a beautiful gilded master-switch which Corporal Gadget, eyes fixed blankly on an elusive point just over Spanner's head, announced that he had Found at the Back of the Château. He was promptly sent back again to see if he could also Discover some Black Enamel, to camouflage it from its rightful owner.

At this point came a summons for Lieutenant Spanner from the General, and he went off, leaving Sapper Satchell to complete the fixing up of the switch. The General, it seemed, had found quite a new area to plan a battle on and wanted some maps of the same at once, please. Taking a note of the section required, Spanner returned at the double, delighted to have a chance of testing Mr. Smith out.

When Sapper Satchell, inside the lorry, had got his sheets of paper out, fitted the plate on to the cylinder and generally got the machine ready, Spanner shouted out to switch on for printing, and went round to the front to start the engine. . . .

Quite what Sapper Satchell had done, we never found out. Evidently he had crossed some wires somewhere. He had also left Mr. Smith in gear. . . .

Spanner luckily had presence of mind enough to fling himself aside. He picked himself up just in time to see Mr. Smith charging out of the main gate and straight down the road to the centre of the village. In the back was the stolid Sapper Satchell imperturbably trying to feed paper into the printing machine. Apparently he had no idea that his officer was not in front driving him. That it was suddenly found necessary to print maps at twenty m.p.h. down a French country road, did not worry him. All that worried him was that the printing machine, for some reason, though he had switched on, would not work.

Snatching a dispatch-rider's motor-cycle, Spanner set off in pursuit of Mr. Smith. He was not difficult to follow. Through the village outskirts he had blazed a very definite trail of overturned stalls, abandoned bicycles, smashed handcarts, crying children, and inhabitants up lamp-posts. At the cross-roads, however, he had met his Waterloo.

Diagonally athwart the roads and blocking both routes, each of which of course were being used by a battalion on the march, sat Mr. Smith. His nose was in a café window and he wore a check tablecloth on his bonnet. The proprietor was trying to charge a casual infantry major for spilt beer, as being the senior British officer in sight. The close-packed troops were singing a ribald song. A military policeman, with the air of one who is trying to restore his dignity after an unfortunate experience, was dusting the seat of his trousers and speaking severely to Sapper Satchell, who was now in the driving-seat pulling levers in a dreamy sort of way. Nothing had the slightest effect on Mr. Smith's movements, even though his engine was running. But now from his tailboard with clock-work-like regularity map after map came shooting out into the crowd like an evening paper rushing off its final edition.

As Lieutenant Spanner came up Satchell caught his eye helplessly, turned round to salute and trod by accident on the accelerator. The printing machine promptly trebled its output and a positive sea of paper shot out over the assembled troops like autumn leaves in a sudden gust of wind. They stopped singing and cries of: 'Wuxtra-Spusshul,' and 'Oo's won the three-thirty, chum?' rose instead. They then broke into another and even more ribald song. . . .

Both battalions were eventually induced to collaborate to move Mr. Smith bodily; but he didn't run out of paper and petrol till long after the troops had run out of humour and adjectives.

Sapper Satchell, whose unskilled efforts with the switch had caused it all, was had up before the Colonel for inefficiency. Nothing much happened to him, though, because quite early on it turned out that he was hardly to blame. For apparently he wasn't a 'machine-minder' by trade at all—not at least as the term is generally accepted. He had been enlisted as such, because that was what he said he had been, but actually in his civilian employment the only 'machines' he had 'minded' were the slot machines on Southend Pier. Looking after a printing press was therefore a little out of his class, but give him a wallet of coppers and a couple of 'What-Uncle-Saw-in-Paris' machines and you probably couldn't have a better man to slip you change for a bob.

PRINTED BY
JARROLD AND SONS LTD.
NORWICH